Mental Math
in the Middle Grades

Jack A. Hope • Barbara J. Reys • Robert E. Reys

DALE SEYMOUR PUBLICATIONS

Cover design: Jim M'Guinness
Illustrations: Mitchell Rose

This book is published by Dale Seymour Publications®, an imprint of Addison Wesley Longman, Inc.

Dale Seymour Publications
10 Bank Street
White Plains, NY 10602
Customer Service: 800-872-1100

Order number DS91615
ISBN 0-86651-312-4

16 17 18 19 20 -ML- 02 01 00 99 98

This Book Is Printed
on Recycled Paper

CONTENTS

PREFACE

Learning to calculate mentally, without the use of external memory aids (including paper and pencil), has many benefits.

1. **Calculating in your head is a practical life skill.** Many types of everyday computation problems can be solved mentally. In fact, practically speaking, many *must* be solved mentally, since we often need to make quick computations when we don't have a calculator or paper and pencil at hand. For example: You are at the airport. The departure board indicates that your flight is scheduled to leave at 3:35. Your watch shows that it's now 2:49. How much time do you have? Enough time to grab a snack? Here's another example: You find tuna fish on sale at the supermarket for 69 cents a can. You would like to stock up now, but you know that you have only $10 with you, and you also need to buy bread and milk. How many cans of tuna could you buy on sale? These and similar situations demonstrate the everyday utility of mental math skills.

2. **Skill at mental math can make written computation easier or quicker.** A student who is dependent on written algorithms might calculate 1000×945 this way:

$$
\begin{array}{r}
1000 \\
\times\ 945 \\
\hline
5000 \\
4000 \\
9000 \\
\hline
945{,}000
\end{array}
$$

Knowing how to "tack on trailing zeros," a mental math skill, can reduce that process to one step: $\mathbf{1000} \times 945 = 945{,}000$. Similarly, faced with the addition of long columns of figures, even with a pencil in hand, the mental math skill "searching for compatible pairs" can simplify the computation. For example, finding numbers that sum to ten makes this addition quicker than taking it step by step:

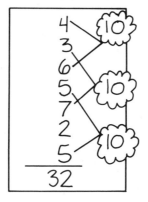

In these and many other ways, mental math skills can streamline students' written work and increase their understanding at the same time.

3. **Proficiency in mental math contributes to increased skill in estimation.** Estimation has come to be recognized as an important part of the mathematics curriculum. It is essential for checking the reasonableness of an answer obtained through the use of a calculator, and estimation skills are useful in solving many everyday problems as well. Mental calculation provides the cornerstone for all estimation processes, offering a variety of alternative algorithms and nonstandard techniques for finding answers.

4. **Mental calculation can lead to a better understanding of place value, mathematical operations, and basic number properties.** Students often do written computation mechanically, without a great deal of thought, simply applying the written algorithms with very little sense of what they are *really* doing. Efficient paper-and-pencil calculation demands careful attention to digits and bookkeeping rules and contributes to a fragmentary view of number relationships. Mental computation, on the other hand, forces students to think about numbers and number relationships. As students learn to manipulate numbers in their heads, they develop a keen number sense and experience increased confidence in their mathematical abilities. Such confidence ensures that these students will not have to turn to a machine or pencil and paper for every straightforward calculation they encounter in daily life.

Despite its many attractive benefits, mental calculation has not played a prominent role in most contemporary mathematics programs. Because of this neglect, most people are not very proficient mental calculators. Recent studies have demonstrated that a large majority of children and young adults cannot perform even the simplest mental calculations. For example, the third National Assessment of Educational Progress in mathematics found that less than half of the 13-year-old sample correctly calculated the product of 60 and 70 "in the head" within 9 seconds. According to the same survey, most children were unaware that a mental calculation is often the most convenient method of solution. For example, only 38 percent of the 13-year-olds thought that the exercise 945×1000 should be done mentally; the majority claimed that either a pencil and paper or a calculator was needed to determine the solution.

Undoubtedly, this performance reflects the current lack of attention given to mental computation by textbook publishers and curriculum developers. To counter this we offer the *Mental Math* series, a planned program of instruction in mental calculation that complements any current elementary school mathematics program. We think you will find the lessons fun and easy to teach. Used regularly, with plenty of practice, these materials can turn your whole class into "mentalmathletes."

Jack Hope
Barbara Reys
Robert Reys

INTRODUCTION

About the *Mental Math* Series

Mental Math in the Middle Grades is the second in a series of three books designed to help teach students the techniques of "figuring in your head."

The first book in the series, suited for students in grades one through three, focuses on simple calculation with whole numbers. These lessons help students develop good reasoning strategies to learn and remember the basic facts of addition and subtraction. Visual aids such as dot patterns, a ten-frame and counters, and the 100 chart figure prominently in the primary grades book.

This second book, designed for grades four through six, extends the skills developed in the preceding book to more difficult mental calculations with whole numbers. The third book, intended for grades six through eight, contains more advanced lessons that introduce methods of calculating mentally with fractions, decimals, and percents, as well as whole numbers.

Features of This Book

Mental Math in the Middle Grades contains 36 lessons in mental calculation, providing for about one lesson a week.

The book is divided into four units. Each unit opens with a "Mental-mathletes" page, featuring general interest anecdotes about experts in mental calculation. These pages can be presented on the overhead and then posted on the bulletin board to stimulate student interest in mental math skills.

There are 9 lessons in each unit. A lesson consists of two reproducible pages: *a lesson page* that you can use to introduce each new mental math strategy, and a *Power Builder* page with two sets of practice problems.

Lesson Page

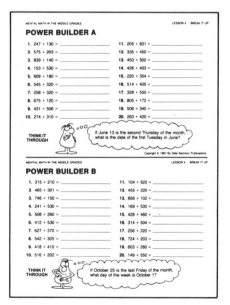

Power Builder Sets

1

At the close of each unit, a review page focuses class discussion on the strategies presented in that unit, to prepare students for the unit progress test.

A section of teaching notes at the front of the book offers helpful tips for presenting each lesson, plus additional problems to use for oral practice. In addition to the unit progress tests, a cumulative test appears in two forms for use in pre- and post-testing. Answer keys for the Power Builder practice sets and all the tests are included at the back of the book.

Teaching Mental Math

SCHEDULING THE LESSONS

If the *Mental Math* program is to be effective, you must incorporate instruction, discussion, and practice into your daily lesson plans. Here is a suggested schedule, based on one lesson a week:

DAY 1: Present the new lesson.
DAY 2: Hand out the first practice set (Power Builder A).
DAYS 3 AND 4: Reinforce the new strategy with oral practice sessions lasting 2–5 minutes.
DAY 5: Hand out the second practice set (Power Builder B).

PLANNING THE LESSONS

The lesson pages have been set in large-size type for display on the overhead projector, a teaching mode that is especially appropriate for presenting mental math strategies. If you are not comfortable with this approach, you could present the lesson at the board or as a class handout. To prepare for each lesson:

1. Duplicate the appropriate masters, either as transparencies or handouts, as needed—both the lesson page and the Power Builder sets. Power Builder pages are designed to be cut in half for distribution at different times.
2. Preview the lesson and the teaching notes. The notes generally give you the rationale behind the lesson and will alert you to important considerations and occasional pitfalls in the new strategy being presented.
3. Consider collecting a number of problems from the Power Builder sets of previous lessons; these can serve as a brief mental warm-up for the students before you begin a new lesson.

PRESENTING THE LESSONS

Discussion Is Critical

As you teach each new lesson, be sure to spend plenty of time developing and discussing the new strategy. This discussion should continue as you proceed to the "TRY THESE . . ." practice problems in the box at the bottom of the lesson page. The TRY THESE excercises are an important part of the instruction. At this stage you are not working on *speed* in mental calculation; you are working on *understanding*. With each problem, pause to discuss the students' answers and their methods of solution. If there are wrong answers, take time to explore how students got them. Through such discussion, you can quickly diagnose and correct the source of any difficulties.

As you will discover, class discussion is a critical part of teaching mental math because there is no other way for students to "show their work." It's all taking place in their heads, and talking about their thought processes is the only way to find out how well they understand the strategies.

Here's another reason that discussion should play a dominant role in the teaching of mental math skills: there is no single "right" way to do a problem in your head. Several alternative methods may be equally practical and efficient. To develop flexibility in thinking about numbers and number relationships, students should learn to look for and recognize a variety of approaches to the same problem. During discussion, encourage students to share different strategies and talk about the advantages of each. If you are a practiced mental calculator yourself, you may have additional tips for the students based on your own techniques.

Stress Visual Thinking

Another important aspect of teaching mental math is developing mental imagery that helps students perform computation in their heads. Too often, students who are asked to do a mental computation simply try to envision the problem as if they were working with pencil and paper. This is often accompanied by physical motions, so that you might see, for example, students using their fingers to "write" the problem in the air or on the desk. Such dependence on familiar paper-and-pencil methods is awkward and ignores many number properties than can simplify mental calculation.

Use concrete materials such as *place value charts* and *money,* which can suggest new ways of thinking about and visualizing computation problems. *Number lines* are often helpful in visualizing addition and subtraction, and *spirals* or *repeating patterns* can help students visualize multiplication. As you discuss the mental math strategies, encourage students to share the way they "see" a problem in their mind's eye.

Help Students Take "Thinking Shortcuts"

Students are often inclined to approach computation problems on a laborious digit-by-digit basis, methodically plodding along in certain rote patterns. Teach them that they need not say (or think) to themselves every digit and every step of the computation process.

That is, faced with a problem of column addition like the one shown here, they should not have to think to themselves:
"4 plus 6 is 10, plus 7 is 17, plus 2 is 19. . . . "
Instead, they should be able to look at the numbers and think simply:
"10 . . . 17 . . . 19 . . ." and so forth.
Often the lesson pages demonstrate such "thinking shortcuts," saying "Here's how a mental math pro thinks. . . ." Model such short-cut thinking for the students as often as you can.

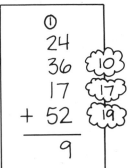

PRACTICING THE STRATEGIES

The two sets of Power Builder exercises with each lesson provide independent practice with specific strategies. As you move from group discussion to independent work, continue to insist that the problems be done *mentally*. When working on the Power Builders, students will need pencils to record their answers, but that is *all* the pencils should be used for.

At first, you may want to circulate around the classroom to enforce the "in your head" rule while students are working on the practice sets. You might also set a time limit so that students won't have time for paper-and-pencil computation. Push them to complete each Power Builder set as rapidly as possible. Three or four minutes is a reasonable target time, but you may need to adjust this to the difficulty of the problems and the abilities of your students. The best timing standards can be determined by experimenting with your class. You might allow more time for Power Builder A sets than for Power Builder B.

At the end of each Power Builder set is a problem called "Think It Through." These problems are generally more difficult than the practice problems, but students still should be able to solve them using mental math. These are to be done *after* the practice problems, and need not be completed within the time limit you have set. Note that a "Think It Through" problem does not necessarily involve the mental math strategy taught in that particular lesson.

OFFERING RELATED PRACTICE

Regular drill of the basic facts of addition, subtraction, multiplication, and division should be used to complement the *Mental Math* program. A daily three-minute oral drill helps students master these important number combinations. Such a drill can serve as a brief warm-up before you teach a *Mental Math* lesson.

Show students how to use mental math strategies to help recall a difficult basic fact. For example, the multiplication fact $8 \times 7 = 56$ can be learned easily by thinking "double the 4's fact." That is, "double $4 \times 7 =$ double $28 = 56$." Good recall of basic facts is essential for proficient mental calculation; at the same time, learning to calculate mentally can help with recall of basic facts. Encourage students to use mental calculation whenever the opportunity arises in a regular mathematics lesson, as well as lessons in other subject areas. Try not to discourage them from using shortcut mental methods to eliminate steps in written calculations. Instead, challenge them to use mental techniques to solve all or part of a problem before they reach for a pencil or a calculator.

Demonstrate the power and usefulness of mental math in making estimates. You might also show how mental calculation can often be used to improve the accuracy of a first rough estimate.

Challenge your class to look through magazines, newspapers, and advertising flyers for examples of real-world uses of mental math. You might display such examples on a bulletin board along with the "Mental-mathlete" pages, illustrating applications of mental calculation and estimation.

Some students will catch on to mental math strategies more quickly than others in your class. Encourage these more able calculators to extend the strategies to more difficult problems. You might want to purchase the next level in the *Mental Math* series and assign more challenging strategies and problems to your best mental calculators. While these students are working independently, you can slow your lesson pace to help the less able mental calculators in your class.

USING THE TESTS

The five tests for *Mental Math in the Middle Grades* include a cumulative test that comes in two parallel forms. Administer Form A before you start instruction in mental math and Form B after you have completed the program. Unless they have had prior instruction in mental computation, students are likely to perform very poorly on the pre-test (Form A). Caution them that these exercises may seem very hard, and ask them simply to do the best they can. Comparing the results of the two tests (Form A and Form B) will demonstrate the improvement in students' ability to calculate mentally.

In addition, there are four progress tests for use throughout the school year, one at the end of each unit. Administer the appropriate test shortly after a unit has been taught and practiced. Regular testing reminds students that mental computation is important and something you value.

Be sure to prepare students for these progress tests with a thorough review of the strategies presented in the preceding unit. The review teaching page for each unit can serve as a starting point for class discussion. In most of their other practice, students will have been concentrating on one operation and one clearly identified strategy at a time. In order to perform with reasonable speed on the progress tests, they will need practice with mixed groups of problems, learning to quickly identify an efficient solution strategy.

There are a number of ways that each test can be presented and timed:

1. **As a handout.** Duplicate and distribute a copy of the test to each student. To time the students, you can write the elapsed time every 10 seconds on the board or an overhead transparency. When a student completes the test, he or she records the most recent elapsed time on the test paper. Alternative ways of presenting elapsed time to a classroom of students are to display cards with easily seen numbers (such as 10 seconds, 20 seconds, and so forth) or to cross out numbers that you have written on a transparency or the board.

2. **As an oral test.** Read aloud each problem on the test, presenting them at a fixed rate (for example, one every 10 seconds). A tape player is an effective way of presenting a test orally because you can carefully control the time per question and you are free during the test to circulate around the classroom. When you give a test orally, students can write their answers on notebook paper.

3. **As a visual presentation.** You might present a test one item at a time, using an overhead transparency or flash cards with easily read figures. In this method, you control the timing by displaying each problem for a brief period (such as 10 seconds), then going on to the next one. Again, students will use a blank sheet of notebook paper to record their answers.

Just before giving any test, remind the students to use only *mental* methods to calculate their answers. You might tap your forehead periodically throughout the test and say "In your head" as a gentle reminder.

LESSON 1   ONE STEP AT A TIME
Mental math skill: Adding multiples of powers of ten

Many good mental math strategies involve working with numbers expressed as powers of ten. Students need to be able to manipulate such numbers mentally without losing track of place value. The transparency for this lesson emphasizes two elements of mental math:

1. Saying aloud to yourself or thinking the place value names, "4 HUNDRED plus 2 HUNDRED," to help focus your attention on the place value involved.

2. Taking each problem one step at a time, number by number—a mental math technique that minimizes the amount of data you have to keep in your head as you work through a problem.

In the TRY THESE problems, some students might discover that it's easier for them to add numbers of the largest place value first, rather than adding the numbers in left-to-right order. For example, for number 3, we could think "5 hundred plus 4 hundred is 9 hundred, plus 30 is 930." This approach works well when students can see the problems; however, when problems are presented orally, taking the problem step by step is the preferred approach.

Problems for oral practice:

1. 500 + 200 + 60
2. 100 + 700 + 50
3. 200 + 500 + 10
4. 700 + 30 + 200
5. 400 + 50 + 100
6. 600 + 80 + 400
7. 30 + 500 + 200
8. 20 + 600 + 200
9. 60 + 100 + 600
10. 5000 + 400 + 300
11. 4000 + 500 + 3000
12. 30 + 500 + 1000

LESSON 2   USING PLACE VALUE NAMES
Mental math skill: Adding multiples of powers of ten

To work computation problems mentally, students need to recognize at a glance which digits have the same place value; they must also be able to name that place value. To help them practice this, you can write pairs of three- or four-digit numbers on the board. Circle one digit. Ask students to name the place value and identify the digit with the same place value in the other number.

The transparency for this lesson demonstrates how students might focus on place value names as they add in their heads.

For problems like number 3 in TRY THESE, check to be sure students understand that "13 hundred 30" is the same as "1 thousand 3 hundred 30."

Problems for oral practice:

1. 340 + 600
2. 510 + 200
3. 450 + 700
4. 700 + 230
5. 100 + 460
6. 900 + 270
7. 7000 + 340
8. 6200 + 500
9. 7300 + 300
10. 200 + 7600
11. 500 + 4200
12. 4100 + 900

LESSON 3   USING WHAT YOU KNOW
Mental math skill: Using basic addition facts in adding multi-digit numbers

This transparency demonstrates to students how they can use basic single-digit addition facts—something that they know automatically—as a bridge to help them add similar numbers with more digits. Some students may need your guidance in seeing how 8 + 6 is similar to 18 + 6, or 38 + 6, or 580 + 60. For practice in recognizing such similarities, ask them to choose a basic single-digit addition fact and to write other computation problems of their own that are similar to the basic fact. For example, a student who chooses 4 + 7 might write such similar problems as 14 + 7, 74 + 7, 124 + 7, 40 + 370, and so on.

Problems for oral practice:
1. 38 + 9
2. 58 + 9
3. 88 + 9
4. 280 + 90
5. 47 + 6
6. 87 + 6
7. 870 + 60
8. 370 + 60
9. 86 + 8
10. 106 + 8
11. 560 + 80
12. 760 + 80

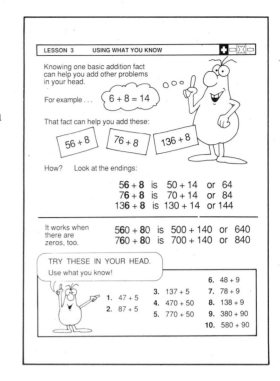

LESSON 4   BREAK IT UP
Mental math skill: Adding by expanding the second addend (when no regrouping is needed)

The task of adding multi-digit numbers in your head can be simplified if you expand or "break up" one of the numbers and then add the parts one step at a time. As a warm-up to the transparency, ask students to mentally add 45 and 20. When they have an answer, say "Now add 3." Point out that they have just mentally computed 45 + 23, but that you helped them by first breaking up the second number (breaking 23 into 20 + 3) so that they could add easier parts in two steps.

The transparency demonstrates expanding the second addend. However, it also works to expand the first addend, as you can demonstrate with examples from the TRY THESE problems.

As an extension of this lesson, you might show how expanding the numbers can help when mentally adding numbers in a series. For example:

TO ADD: 23 + 12 + 21 + 13

$$10 + 2 \quad 20 + 1 \quad 10 + 3$$

THINK: 23 ... 33, 35 ... 55, 56 ... 66, 69

This technique also can be used to speed up column addition, looking at both tens and ones digits instead of adding all the ones first.

```
  23      23 . . .
  12      33, 35 . . .
  21      55, 56 . . .
+ 13      66, 69
```

Problems for oral practice:
1. 37 + 50 + 2
2. 43 + 60 + 4
3. 65 + 20 + 2
4. 124 + 30 + 3
5. 327 + 40 + 2
6. 604 + 30 + 5
7. 281 + 400 + 5
8. 609 + 40 + 1
9. 213 + 60 + 5
10. 516 + 30 + 3
11. 425 + 300 + 20
12. 563 + 200 + 30

LESSON 5   BREAK IT UP
Mental math skill: Adding by expanding the second addend (when regrouping is needed)

Students accustomed to familiar written algorithms for addition with regrouping will often try to resort to that approach in their heads. That is, a student might think laboriously, "Add 28 + 17 . . . 8 plus 7 is 15, write 5, carry 1, 2 plus 1 is 3, plus 1 is 4, write 4, answer is 45."

This transparency demonstrates an alternative way of thinking about such computations—a way that works much better for mental math. As in lesson 4, students are encouraged to break up the second addend, then add the parts. There may be some students who will stumble at adding even 38 and 7 mentally. (If so, they need more practice with lesson 3). You might suggest that even further expansion could work for them; that is, think of 7 as 5 + 2; then 38 + 2 is 40, plus 5 is 45.

Problems for oral practice:

1. 38 + 40 + 3
2. 76 + 30 + 5
3. 84 + 50 + 9
4. 29 + 70 + 3
5. 45 + 30 + 2
6. 38 + 40 + 5
7. 21 + 50 + 9
8. 17 + 30 + 5
9. 67 + 80 + 8
10. 23 + 70 + 5
11. 55 + 40 + 8
12. 43 + 20 + 7

LESSON 6   DROPPING COMMON ZEROS
Mental math skill: Subtracting multiples of powers of ten

With the strategy demonstrated on this transparency, the danger is losing track of the place value in the process of dropping and replacing common zeros. You might use the TRY THESE problems or others like them for practice in place value, asking students to name the place value of the front-end or leading digit in each number.

Before doing the TRY THESE problems, extend the "dropping common zeros" idea to a multi-step subtraction problem: "Our school had $800. We spent $300 on the school picnic and $200 on a school play. How much money do we have left?" Help students see how to take it one step at a time, dropping common zeros for ease of computing mentally: 8 minus 3 is 5, minus 2 is 3, or $300 left.

Problems for oral practice:

1. 300 − 200
2. 900 − 600
3. 500 − 40
4. 300 − 80
5. 2000 − 500
6. 5000 − 2000
7. 8000 − 500
8. 5000 − 2000 − 400
9. 4000 − 300 − 200
10. 7000 − 200 − 2000
11. 5000 − 400 − 30
12. 6000 − 300 − 10

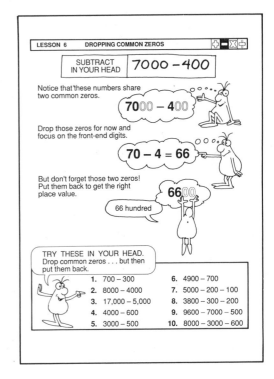

LESSON 7   DROPPING COMMON ZEROS
Mental math skill: Subtracting multiples of ten

Once again, when applying the strategy of dropping common zeros prior to subtraction, a clear sense of place value is critical for students' success. You can call attention to the importance of place value in mental subtraction with a money problem: "I saved $87.54 and spent $30 for a robot-car. How much money do I have left?" You might ask questions like these: "What is the place value of the digits we subtract? Why does the number of cents remain unchanged as we work this problem?"

The transparency also makes a point that you should repeatedly emphasize to your students: that there is probably more than one way to do any problem in your head. There is no "right" or "wrong" way to mentally calculate, as long as the resulting answer is accurate. Encourage students to share and discuss different mental computation strategies. Then help them gain the confidence to find and use the mental math techniques or "short cuts" that work best for them.

Problems for oral practice:

1.	400 – 20	**7.**	4300 – 200
2.	730 – 200	**8.**	740 – 30
3.	560 – 100	**9.**	750 – 50
4.	4800 – 700	**10.**	1200 – 800
5.	5500 – 400	**11.**	7300 – 500
6.	580 – 70	**12.**	4800 – 900

LESSON 8   FRONT-END FOCUS
Mental math skill: Subtracting numbers with the same ending digits

In a subtraction problem, when the ending digits are the same in both numbers, we can use a strategy similar to dropping common zeros and deal with only the front-end (lead) digits. Help students see how this procedure works by presenting a money problem: "I earned $64 and spent $24 on gifts. How much do I have left?" Discuss with them what happens to the ending digits, and how to determine the correct place value.

In the TRY THESE problems, students should be alert to the fact that sometimes several ending digits are the same, and sometimes only the last digits.

Problems for oral practice:

1.	76 – 6	**7.**	648 – 348
2.	98 – 8	**8.**	226 – 126
3.	27 – 17	**9.**	438 – 238
4.	86 – 36	**10.**	586 – 186
5.	412 – 2	**11.**	749 – 209
6.	527 – 7	**12.**	814 – 304

LESSON 9   ONE STEP AT A TIME
Mental math skill: Adding and subtracting multiples of ten

In lesson 1, students practiced adding multiples of ten in chains; here they practice the same step-by-step approach in chains with mixed addition and subtraction. Real-life problems often involve chaining of this type.

As a mental warm-up for this type of problem, have students practice skip counting by tens and by twenties, both forwards and backwards. Students' ability to deal mentally with multiples of ten will be useful in many different mental math strategies. Orally presented problems of this type will also help students see the value of doing one step at a time.

Problems for oral practice:

1. 70 + 10 − 30
2. 60 − 30 + 40
3. 10 + 50 − 30
4. 80 − 40 − 10 + 30
5. 50 + 30 − 20 − 20
6. 20 + 70 − 50 − 10
7. 40 − 20 + 60 − 10
8. 70 − 70 + 40 + 20
9. 10 + 60 − 40 + 10
10. 60 + 30 − 20 − 50
11. 40 − 30 − 10 + 70
12. 90 − 20 + 10 − 40

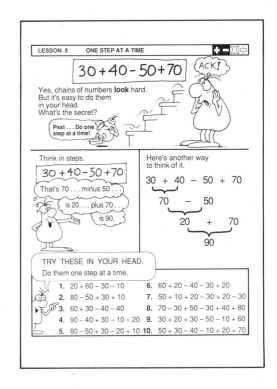

UNIT ONE REVIEW

To prepare students for the Unit One progress test, help them review the mental math strategies presented in lessons 1–9. Go over the mental math techniques listed in the box at left, working through the sample problems together. In the numbered review exercises, encourage discussion of different strategies that could be used for the same problem.

Students will need to pick up speed with the new strategies if they are to succeed on the timed test. Plan to give them some timed practice with problems you select at random from the Power Builder sets for lessons 1–9. You can present these orally or write them on the board, erasing them after a set length of time. Gradually shorten the time you allow for selecting a strategy and computing the answer.

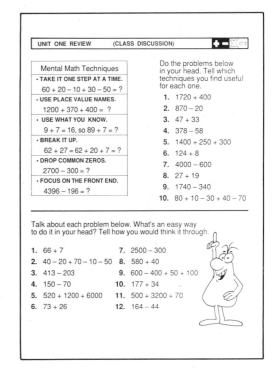

LESSON 10 STARTING AT THE LEFT
Mental math skill: Adding from the front end (when regrouping is needed)

This lesson has the same goal as lesson 5: to help students mentally add two-digit numbers when regrouping is needed. This lesson, however, offers a new strategy—starting at the left—that helps students think of the problem in place value terms. That is, students add the tens and ones separately, then add those sums to get the correct total.

After students have practiced this strategy on the TRY THESE problems, ask them to look at the same problems with the "break it up" strategy (expanding one of the numbers) in mind. Ask them which strategy they prefer, making clear that neither one is "better" than the other—it's a matter of personal choice.

As an extension, offer them some three- and four-digit addition problems that need regrouping (269 + 138; 154 + 849) to demonstrate that "starting at the left" works well with larger numbers, too.

Problems for oral practice:
1. 37 + 28
2. 42 + 39
3. 43 + 25
4. 84 + 25
5. 19 + 43
6. 27 + 36
7. 48 + 35
8. 36 + 48
9. 27 + 72
10. 35 + 79
11. 84 + 66
12. 96 + 43

LESSON 11 STARTING AT THE LEFT
Mental math skill: Subtracting from the front end (when no regrouping is needed)

In this lesson, the "starting at the left" strategy is discussed in terms of "starting at the front end." Students should understand that these mean the same thing. The "starting at the left" (or front end) strategy works well for subtraction problems when no regrouping is required. Doing some warm-up practice with subtraction problems involving multiples of ten (such as 45 – 30, 87 – 50, 440 – 140) helps students focus on the front-end digits, a natural lead-in to this lesson.

In order to decide if the front-end approach will work for any given subtraction problem, students need to be able to recognize whether or not regrouping is involved. If students need practice with this, present a series of subtraction problems either visually (on the board) or orally, asking of each one, "Need regrouping or not?" For example:

48 – 23 (no)	72 – 16 (yes)	97 – 35 (no)
947 – 235 (no)	463 – 299 (yes)	390 – 155 (yes)
4173 – 3186 (yes)	2522 – 1401 (no)	7311 – 4200 (no)

Problems for oral practice:
1. 38 – 25
2. 86 – 34
3. 45 – 31
4. 98 – 75
5. 37 – 25
6. 84 – 63
7. 78 – 46
8. 224 – 213
9. 568 – 535
10. 427 – 415
11. 639 – 628
12. 785 – 741

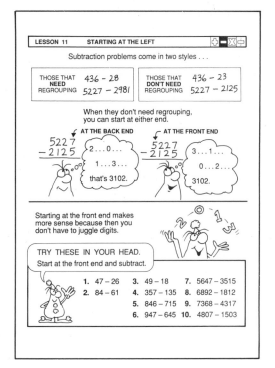

LESSON 12 WORKING WITH FIVES

Mental math skill: Adding by expanding to numbers ending in five

Asking students to do some skip counting by five will prepare them for this lesson. You might also ask students to give you a two-digit number; then say "Add ten" and ask them for the sum.

The first example on the transparency demonstrates the mental process of adding two numbers that end in five—simply find the sum of the front-end digits and then add ten. Although this is not shown as a separate step in the second example where we mentally add 35 + 45, students should recognize that they can think 30 + 40 = 70, plus 10 = 80. This step can be abbreviated to 3 + 4 = 7, 7 + 1 = 8, so 80.

Compare this strategy with the one presented in lesson 4, where we expanded one addend to get "easier parts," usually one ending in zero. "Working with fives" is a variation on that strategy; it shows students that numbers ending in five can be almost as easy to work with mentally as numbers ending in zero.

Problems for oral practice:

1. 35 + 45		**7.** 36 + 45	
2. 25 + 65		**8.** 27 + 65	
3. 85 + 15		**9.** 85 + 17	
4. 35 + 25		**10.** 35 + 26	
5. 45 + 55		**11.** 45 + 58	
6. 15 + 65		**12.** 16 + 65	

LESSON 13 TRADING OFF

Mental math skill: Adding by making multiples of ten and adjusting (compensation)

The first exercise introduces *compatible numbers*—in this case, pairs of numbers that "make ten." (In the exercise below, we "make tens" by adding 2 to 38.) If this concept is new to your students, you might give them further practice in identifying such compatible pairs. Call out a one- or two-digit number and ask what number we can add to "make tens."

Be sure that students understand the steps of trading off:
1. "Make tens" by adding a compatible number to the addend.
2. Adjust the other addend to compensate, subtracting the same amount from it.
3. Add the two adjusted addends.

The number lines offer a visual reference for students, helping them see the process in their minds.

As a variation on this strategy, some students might feel more comfortable adjusting the total at the end of the process, rather than adjusting both addends. That is, to add 38 + 45, a student might think "38 + 2 = 40, 40 + 45 = 85, and 85 − 2 = 83." Neither strategy is "better" than the other; students should be encouraged to use whichever approach works for them.

Problems for oral practice:

1. 29 + 63		**7.** 37 + 69	
2. 38 + 45		**8.** 43 + 49	
3. 48 + 27		**9.** 56 + 19	
4. 59 + 64		**10.** 29 + 28	
5. 69 + 75		**11.** 43 + 58	
6. 59 + 27		**12.** 54 + 98	

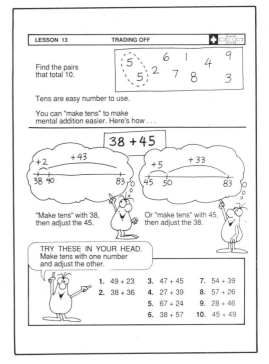

LESSON 12 WORKING WITH FIVES

It's easy to add in your head when both numbers end in 5.

65 + 25

1. Add the tens. 60 + 20 = 80
2. Add the ones. 5 + 5 = 10
3. Find the total. 80 + 10 = 90

The answer will always end in zero!

Here's a trick to help add numbers in your head . . .

35 + 48

Expand to make them both end in 5 . . . then add what's left over.

35 + 48
45 + 3
35 + 45 + 3
80 + 3 . . . 83

TRY THESE IN YOUR HEAD.
Make both numbers end in 5.

1. 46 + 25	3. 55 + 27	7. 135 + 26
2. 17 + 45	4. 46 + 15	8. 145 + 19
	5. 39 + 85	9. 235 + 37
	6. 75 + 38	10. 55 + 38

LESSON 13 TRADING OFF

Find the pairs that total 10.

5 6 1 4 9
5 2 7 8 3

Tens are easy number to use.

You can "make tens" to make mental addition easier. Here's how . . .

38 + 45

+2 +43
38 40 83

+5 +33
45 50 83

"Make tens" with 38, then adjust the 45.

Or "make tens" with 45, then adjust the 38.

TRY THESE IN YOUR HEAD.
Make tens with one number and adjust the other.

1. 49 + 23	3. 47 + 45	7. 54 + 39
2. 38 + 36	4. 27 + 39	8. 57 + 26
	5. 67 + 24	9. 28 + 46
	6. 38 + 57	10. 45 + 49

LESSON 14   BALANCING IN SUBTRACTION
Mental math skill: Subtracting by making multiples of ten and adjusting (compensation)

In order to be comfortable with this strategy, students need to understand *renaming subtraction*. Write a simple problem on the board and demonstrate what happens to the difference when we rename the problem by adding the same amount to both numbers.

PROBLEM	ADD 1	ADD 2	ADD 3	ADD 4
6 $-\,2$ 4	7 $-\,3$ 4	8 $-\,4$ 4	9 $-\,5$ 4	10 $-\,6$ 4

If students understand that the difference is unchanged, they should have no trouble accepting the "balancing" strategy presented on this transparency.

Be sure students understand that we want to "make tens" with the number we are subtracting (the subtrahend), *not* with the one we are subtracting from (the minuend). The point here is that it's easy to subtract a multiple of ten (ending in zero) from another number.

Problems for oral practice:
1. 65 – 48
2. 42 – 19
3. 74 – 29
4. 93 – 78
5. 60 – 38
6. 25 – 17
7. 45 – 28
8. 82 – 59
9. 81 – 47
10. 90 – 68
11. 123 – 89
12. 325 – 99

LESSON 15   SEARCHING FOR COMPATIBLES
Mental math skill: Identifying pairs that sum to 100 and 1000 (or compatible numbers)

Students had a brief introduction to compatible numbers in lesson 13, where they identified pairs of single-digit numbers that "make ten." This lesson extends the strategy to two- and three-digit numbers that "make 100" and "make 1000." Finding compatible numbers (numbers that are easy to mentally compute) is a very useful mental math strategy. Lessons 15-18 work with the use of compatible numbers in addition; later lessons will explore the use of compatible numbers in multiplication. Of course, while the focus of this lesson is *addition,* compatible numbers help with mental subtraction, too. That is, if you recognize the compatibles 85 and 15, the answer to 100 – 85 is easy.

Give extra practice in a money context. Say, "I'm going to tell you how much money I have. You tell me how much more I need to make one dollar." Then name various amounts, such as 75 cents, 32 cents, 91 cents, 40 cents, 28 cents, 52 cents. Show how this technique can be used to determine the change from a purchase. For example: 32-cent purchase, pay with one dollar, change is 68 cents (a compatible number).

Problems for oral practice:
1. 40 + 60
2. 50 + 50
3. 30 + 70
4. 28 + 72
5. 100 – 54
6. 100 – 73
7. 450 + 550
8. 200 + 800
9. 410 + 590
10. 1000 – 750
11. 1000 – 380
12. 1000 – 225

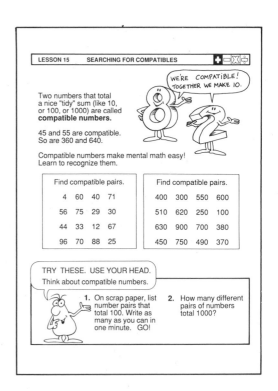

LESSON 16 SEARCHING FOR COMPATIBLES
Mental math skill: Identifying compatible numbers for various multiples of ten

This lesson extends the idea of compatible numbers to mean any pair that makes a "tidy" sum, such as 50, 200, 300, 500. As in lesson 15, discuss how compatible numbers can help with subtraction as well as addition: $50 - 35$, $200 - 130$, $300 - 40$, $500 - 125$. You can provide extra practice with money amounts using the same basic approach suggested for lesson 15. This time, for each amount you name, ask students to name the amount needed to total 50 cents, or $2, or $5, or $10. Again point out how this technique can be used to determine change from a purchase.

Problems for oral practice:
1. $42 + 8$
2. $27 + 73$
3. $38 + 12$
4. $20 + 280$
5. $46 + 4$
6. $140 + 60$
7. $35 + 165$
8. $210 + 90$
9. $200 - 47$
10. $50 - 12$
11. $300 - 50$
12. $500 - 130$

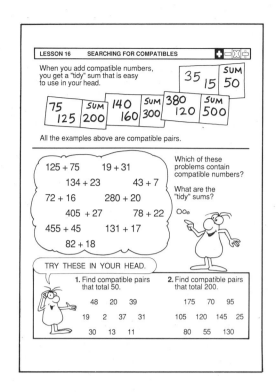

LESSON 17 SEARCHING FOR COMPATIBLES
Mental math skill: Adding a series of compatible numbers

This lesson demonstrates how to apply the use of compatible numbers when adding a series or chain of numbers. In lesson 1, students learned that they could attack a chain "one step at a time," or number by number. Here they learn an alternative approach—finding compatible pairs within the chain, then adding the "tidy" subtotals plus whatever "untidy" numbers are left over. This strategy works well when problems are presented visually rather than orally.

As a warm-up for this lesson, ask students to add pairs of numbers that are multiples of five and ten, for example: $25 + 30$; $50 + 85$; $65 + 15$; $80 + 45$. Working with numbers ending in zero and five is a crucial mental math skill that crosses over many different strategies. Students should practice until they can add such numbers in their heads quickly and accurately.

Problems for oral practice:
1. $30 + 50 + 20$
2. $40 + 50 + 30$
3. $70 + 40 + 50$
4. $15 + 25 + 40$
5. $35 + 40 + 25$
6. $15 + 60 + 25$
7. $10 + 20 + 30 + 40$
8. $60 + 30 + 15 + 5$
9. $35 + 30 + 20 + 15$
10. $35 + 15 + 5 + 40$
11. $70 + 20 + 5 + 10$
12. $30 + 50 + 15 + 20 + 5$

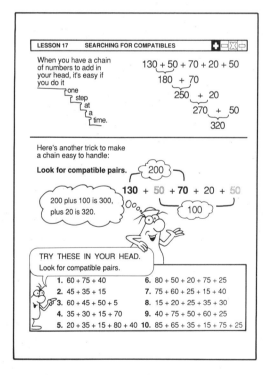

LESSON 18 MAKE-YOUR-OWN COMPATIBLES
Mental math skill: Expanding or using compensation to make compatible pairs for adding

Before trying this lesson, students should be able to readily identify compatible numbers as presented in lessons 15–17; they should be comfortable with the "break it up" strategies (expanding one of the addends) introduced in lessons 4 and 5; and they should be familiar with the variation on "trading off" presented in lesson 13. Here in lesson 18, they are asked to combine such approaches to "make their own" compatible numbers for easier mental addition.

You can give students practice in expanding a number to likely compatibles through a money context. Name an amount of money, such as 52 cents, and ask students to name coins that total that amount. Many answers are possible, but the point is to find the *simplest* breakdown. In this case, a half dollar and two pennies, or two quarters and two pennies, would be reasonable answers. Show how this breakdown could help them mentally add $1.25 and $0.52.

Be sure students understand that whether we *add* or *subtract* a number from the total of our compatible pairs depends on what we have done to the original numbers in order to make the compatible pair.

Problems for oral practice:

1. 26 + 75
2. 77 + 25
3. 25 + 28
4. 52 + 150
5. 75 + 127
6. 26 + 125
7. 175 + 26
8. 28 + 75
9. 225 + 79
10. 125 + 76
11. 17 + 85
12. 325 + 78

UNIT TWO REVIEW

To prepare students for the Unit Two progress test, help them review the mental math strategies presented in lessons 10–18. Go over the mental math techniques listed in the box at left, working through the sample problems together. In the numbered review exercises, encourage discussion of different strategies that could be used for the same problem.

Students will need to pick up speed with the new strategies if they are to succeed on the timed test. Plan to give them some timed practice with problems you select at random from the Power Builder sets for lessons 10–18. You can present these orally or write them on the board, erasing them after a set length of time. Gradually shorten the time you allow for selecting a strategy and computing the answer.

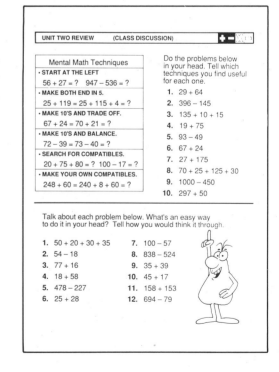

LESSON 19   THINK QUARTERS
Mental math skill: Adding multiples of 25

Skip counting by 25 will prepare students for this lesson. You might time students as they count by 25 to 200 or 500. Then time them again in a day or two and note any improvement.

Recognizing the 25-50-75-00 pattern is an important foundation for mentally adding multiples of 25. Thinking of this pattern as collecting piles of quarters to make dollars can help students do the mental computation.

Sometimes giving students a visual image also helps reinforce the pattern. One such visual pattern (four columns) is shown on the transparency. Alternatively, they might think of the pattern as an ever-increasing spiral, like this:

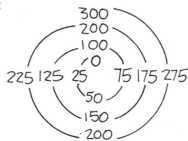

Problems for oral practice:

1. 25 + 25 + 25
2. 25 + 50 + 25
3. 50 + 25 + 50
4. 25 + 50 + 50
5. 75 + 25 + 25
6. 125 + 25 + 25
7. 150 + 25 + 50
8. 175 + 50 + 25
9. 25 + 125 + 50
10. 75 + 50 + 50
11. 25 + 125 + 75
12. 75 + 50 + 25

LESSON 20   NOTICING NINES
Mental math skill: Using compensation when adding numbers ending in eight and nine

This strategy is an alternative to the "trading off" strategy presented in lesson 13. Just as when using that strategy, the students "make tens" to get tidier numbers. Here, the idea is to "make tens" with addends ending in eight or nine, then adjust the total downward to compensate. Thus, $8.99 + $3.99 could be thought of as $9 + $4 = $13, minus 2 cents, or $12.98. (If we were to use "trading off" instead, we would make tens with just one addend and adjust the other before adding. That is, to add $8.99 + $3.99, we would think of it as $9.00 + $3.98, or $12.98.) Ask students to compare the two strategies and think about which one seems easier or more natural to them.

Problems for oral practice

1. 75 + 19
2. 23 + 49
3. 59 + 27
4. 29 + 68
5. 199 + 247
6. 299 + 318
7. 516 + 99
8. 428 + 299
9. $3.75 + $0.99
10. $4.16 + $1.99
11. $0.79 + $0.99
12. $4.99 + $3.99

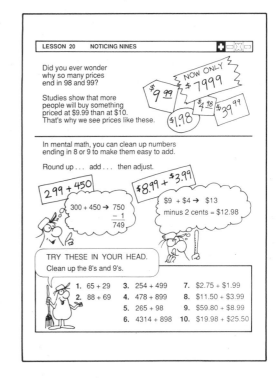

LESSON 21   NOTICING NINES
Mental math skill: Using compensation when subtracting numbers ending in eight and nine

This subtraction strategy is an alternative to the "balancing" strategy presented in lesson 14. In "balancing," the students "make tens" to get a tidier subtrahend and adjust the minuend by the same amount before they subtract. In this new strategy, we still "make tens" of the subtrahend, but we leave the minuend alone and do our adjusting *after* we've subtracted.

One possible confusion in this lesson is that we *add* to adjust the answer; some students may be tempted to *subtract* to compensate, as they did in lesson 20. Discuss this with the students, comparing lessons 20 and 21: In the "noticing nines" strategy, why do we *subtract* to compensate when we're adding, and *add* to compensate when we're subtracting? Talking through each of the processes should reduce the confusion. Using smaller numbers will also clarify the procedure: for example, $17 - 9 = (17 - 10) + 1 = 7 + 1 = 8$.

Problems for oral practice:
1. $76 - 29$
2. $48 - 19$
3. $94 - 59$
4. $73 - 49$
5. $75 - 18$
6. $43 - 28$
7. $416 - 99$
8. $523 - 99$
9. $288 - 99$
10. $416 - 199$
11. $536 - 299$
12. $545 - 98$

LESSON 22   TACK ON TRAILING ZEROS
Mental math skill: Multiplying by powers of ten

This strategy is very basic to mental multiplying and should be practiced extensively. To emphasize the relationship between place value names and trailing zeros, ask students to *name* numbers that you identify this way: 3 followed by three zeros; 7 followed by two zeros; 6 followed by four zeros; 21 followed by three zeros; 35 followed by two zeros. You can also use the reverse procedure: for example, "How many ending zeros in three thousand five hundred? in eight hundred forty? in 27 thousand?" Encourage the use of the words "tack on" as you work through the TRY THESE problems.

Problems for oral practice:
1. 4×100
2. 23×10
3. 16×100
4. 1000×43
5. 28×10
6. 16×1000
7. 100×45
8. 6×1000
9. 14×100
10. 10×389
11. 516×10
12. 427×100

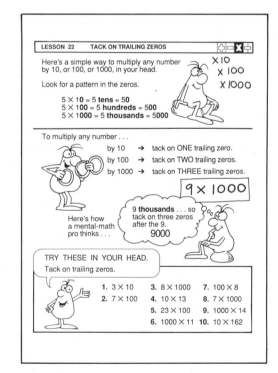

LESSON 23 TACK ON TRAILING ZEROS
Mental math skill: Multiplying when there are trailing zeros in one factor

This lesson presents a simple extension of the strategy introduced in lesson 22. Using the transparency, emphasize the idea of "cutting off" zeros by covering them with a mask or a grease pencil, thereby isolating the other digits. Then uncover them (or rub off the grease pencil) to focus on the zeros that must be "tacked on" to the answer. (If you have prepared a handout for the lesson, you can ask students to use a finger or thumb to physically "cut off" the zeros.)

Problems for oral practice:

1. 4 × 30
2. 70 × 8
3. 40 × 6
4. 5 × 60
5. 9 × 300
6. 20 × 5
7. 8 × 600
8. 500 × 3
9. 12 × 200
10. 5 × 600
11. 40 × 9
12. 200 × 8

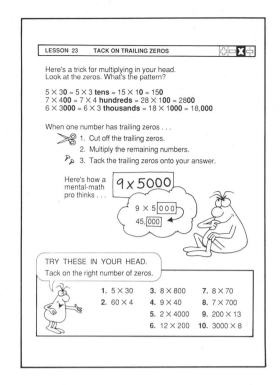

LESSON 24 TACK ON TRAILING ZEROS
Mental math skill: Multiplying when there are trailing zeros in two factors

In this further extension of the strategy presented in lessons 22 and 23, students learn to collect *all* the trailing zeros to tack on when zeros appear in both factors.

One common error in using the "tack on trailing zeros" strategy arises when the leading numbers yield a product that ends in zero itself. For example: in the problem 60 × 500, we cut off the trailing zeros, multiply 6 × 5 = 30, and tack on the zeros again. Sometimes the zero in the 30 gets lost in the mental process and students give the answer 3000 instead of 30,000. If students seem to be having this trouble, work through some problems on the board and give extra practice with similar problems. For example: 500 × 80; 40 × 50,000; 50 × 2000; 800 × 5000; 500 × 400; 20 × 500.

Problems for oral practice:

1. 20 × 60
2. 80 × 50
3. 40 × 70
4. 30 × 60
5. 10 × 400
6. 20 × 200
7. 300 × 6
8. 400 × 60
9. 120 × 30
10. 10 × 300
11. 70 × 200
12. 500 × 70

LESSON 25　FRONT-END MULTIPLYING
Mental math skill: Multiplying by expanding a two-digit factor

Encourage students to see this process as "left-to-right multiplication." That is, first we multiply the tens, then the ones, then add them together. Actually *covering* the digits not being multiplied may help students form a useful mental image of the strategy. In other words, cover the ones digits while you multiply the tens, then cover the tens and expose the ones to multiply those. Students might recognize that they are applying the distributive property.

Problems for oral practice:

1. 23×6	**7.** 26×6
2. 5×45	**8.** 85×3
3. 7×28	**9.** 5×75
4. 15×7	**10.** 4×29
5. 6×46	**11.** 8×43
6. 5×25	**12.** 62×7

LESSON 26　FRONT-END MULTIPLYING
Mental math skill: Multiplying by expanding a three-digit factor

This lesson extends the left-to-right multiplication strategy to three-digit numbers. In order to become comfortable with this strategy, students may need some practice in expanding three-digit numbers. There are different ways to break up such a number, and students should learn to look for a way that will make the problem easy for them to do in their heads. For example, in the second problem on the transparency, 423×3, the number 423 could be broken into $400 + 23$, or $420 + 3$, or $400 + 20 + 3$. Any of these is perfectly acceptable; students should be encouraged to try the different possibilities to discover which seems easiest for them to use.

When you work through the TRY THESE problems as a group, ask students how they would choose to break up the three-digit number in each problem. Emphasize that there is no "right" way, and be supportive of individual variation.

Problems for oral practice:

1. 4×525	**7.** 5×125
2. 6×210	**8.** 5×320
3. 7×408	**9.** 4×325
4. 5×311	**10.** 6×350
5. 7×420	**11.** 5×403
6. 3×430	**12.** 8×309

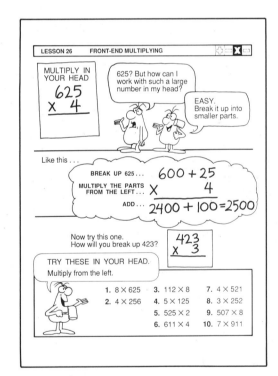

LESSON 27 NOTICING NINES
Mental math skill: Multiplying when one factor ends in nine

For this multiplication strategy, students need to be comfortable with mental subtraction—especially subtraction from numbers ending in zero. Offer some practice with problems like these: 800 – 8; 3000 – 6; 450 – 9; 4500 – 50; $5.40 less 9 cents [$5.40 – $0.09]; $81 less 90 cents [$81.00 – $0.90]. Thinking of money, that is, turning a number like 199 into $1.99 in your head, can sometimes make this strategy seem easier.

Problems for oral practice:
1. 5×99
2. 3×99
3. 4×199
4. 3×199
5. 6×299
6. 2×399
7. $4 \times \$0.99$
8. $2 \times \$0.99$
9. $5 \times \$1.99$
10. $2 \times \$1.99$
11. $7 \times \$3.99$
12. $5 \times \$5.99$

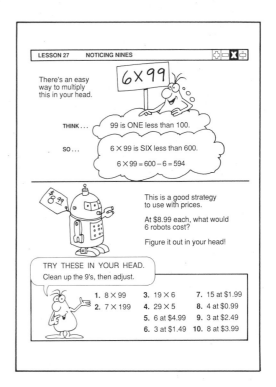

LESSON 27   NOTICING NINES

6 X 99

There's an easy way to multiply this in your head.

THINK . . .   99 is ONE less than 100.

SO . . .   6 × 99 is SIX less than 600.
6 × 99 = 600 − 6 = 594

This is a good strategy to use with prices.

At $8.99 each, what would 6 robots cost?

Figure it out in your head!

TRY THESE IN YOUR HEAD.
Clean up the 9's, then adjust.

1. 8 × 99   3. 19 × 6   7. 15 at $1.99
2. 7 × 199   4. 29 × 5   8. 4 at $0.99
              5. 6 at $4.99 9. 3 at $2.49
              6. 3 at $1.49 10. 8 at $3.99

UNIT THREE REVIEW

To prepare students for the Unit Three progress test, help them review the mental math strategies presented in lessons 19–27. Go over the mental math techniques listed in the box at left, working through the sample problems together. In the numbered review exercises, encourage discussion of different strategies that could be used for the same problem.

Students will need to pick up speed with the new strategies if they are to succeed on the timed test. Plan to give them some timed practice with problems you select at random from the Power Builder sets for lessons 19–27. You can present these orally or write them on the board, erasing them after a set length of time. Gradually shorten the time you allow for selecting a strategy and computing the answer.

UNIT THREE REVIEW   (CLASS DISCUSSION)

Mental Math Techniques
- THINK QUARTERS.
  550 + 125 + 50 = ?
- CLEAN UP 8'S AND 9'S.
  TO ADD . . . 198 + 499 = ?
  TO SUBTRACT . . . 672 − 98 = ?
  TO MULTIPLY . . . 7 × $3.99 = ?
- TACK ON TRAILING ZEROS.
  9 × 100 = ? 60 × 400 = ?
- MULTIPLY FROM THE LEFT.
  8 × 23 = ? 253 × 4 = ?

Do the problems below in your head. Tell which techniques you find useful for each one.
1. 4 × 399
2. 508 × 4
3. $3.47 + $1.99
4. 425 + 75 + 75
5. 7 × 400
6. 733 − 299
7. 247 + 399
8. 5 × $19.99
9. 200 × 900
10. 213 × 3

Talk about each problem below. What's an easy way to do it in your head? Tell how you would think it through.
1. 574 − 98
2. 275 + 50 + 25
3. 5 × 60
4. 8 × 425
5. $45.00 − $14.99
6. 5 × 130
7. 98 + 140
8. 20 × $1.99
9. 150 + 125
10. 30 × 30
11. 8 × 69
12. 50 × 800

LESSON 28   DOUBLING
Mental math skill: Doubling two- and three-digit numbers

This is a relatively simple lesson as most students will have already mastered multiplying by two. For three-digit factors, students may initially need to write down each partial product before adding. As a warm-up before showing the transparency, ask students to double various one-digit numbers as you call them out in rapid succession; then do the same with multiples of 10 and 100.

Doubling is a useful mental math strategy that often helps make a problem easier to do in your head. One example of this will be demonstrated in lesson 29, "Halving and Doubling."

Problems for oral practice:

1. Double 25		**7.** Double 63
2. Double 34		**8.** Double 121
3. Double 24		**9.** Double 130
4. Double 48		**10.** Double 240
5. Double 55		**11.** Double 350
6. Double 35		**12.** Double 450

LESSON 29   HALVING AND DOUBLING
Mental math skill: Multiplying by halving one factor and doubling the other

This lesson demonstrates the usefulness of halving and doubling to make a multiplication problem easier to compute mentally. In addition to being skilled at doubling, students will also need to be able to mentally halve a number (divide it by two). As a warm-up for this lesson, give students practice in doubling various numbers and halving even numbers. Use the words *half* and *double* repeatedly as you lead students through the TRY THESE problems. Help students recognize when a problem needs more than one halving-and-doubling step to make it truly easy to compute in your head.

Problems for oral practice:

1. 4×24		**7.** 5×42
2. 6×250		**8.** 6×450
3. 4×75		**9.** 6×450
4. 5×32		**10.** 50×48
5. 12×250		**11.** 4×72
6. 4×35		**12.** 50×88

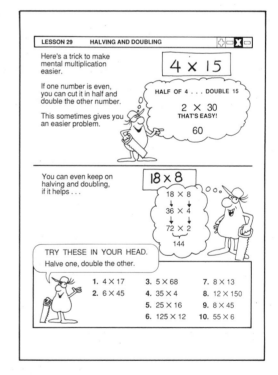

LESSON 30 DIVIDE BY MULTIPLYING

Mental math skill: Dividing by turning the problem around and multiplying

Division takes many different symbolic forms, but the operation is the same regardless of how it looks, and students need to learn how to interpret each form. Because many students find division to be a difficult operation in *written* computation, they may well balk at trying to divide in their heads. Thus you may want to give some extra attention to presenting the mental division techniques in lessons 30–33.

When introducing the "divide by multiplying" strategy, demonstrate it with very simple problems, such as 6 ÷ 2 (2 times what equals 6?); 12 ÷ 3 (3 times what equals 12?); 25 ÷ 5 (5 times what equals 25?). Once students understand the concept, they should have little trouble with the problems in this lesson.

You might want to review the "tack on trailing zeros" strategy presented in lessons 22-24, and ask students how they can use this strategy to determine the place value of the answers to these division problems. As you work through the TRY THESE problems, ask students to think in terms of "[divisor] times *what number* equals [dividend]?"

Problems for oral practice:

1. 700 ÷ 10	**7.** 6000 ÷ 30
2. 480 ÷ 4	**8.** 5000 ÷ 25
3. 300 ÷ 5	**9.** 4200 ÷ 70
4. 200 ÷ 40	**10.** 2100 ÷ 700
5. 270 ÷ 30	**11.** 3000 ÷ 50
6. 450 ÷ 50	**12.** 4800 ÷ 120

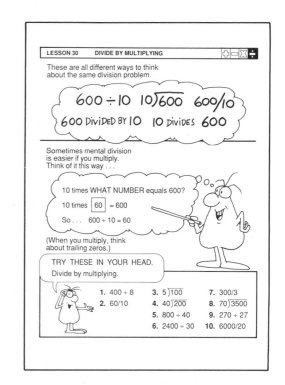

LESSON 31 TACK ON TRAILING ZEROS

Mental math skill: Dividing by single digits when there are trailing zeros in the dividend

Students who have been using the "tack on trailing zeros" strategy in mental multiplication should have little trouble using it in mental division. To help students form a mental image of the process of "cutting off" zeros and "tacking" them back on, use a grease pencil, a mask, or your finger to physically cover up and later expose the zeros.

In the TRY THESE problems, have the students multiply to check their answers. Since mental multiplication is generally easier than mental division, checking by multiplying is always a good policy. In this checking step, we check to see that we tacked on the correct number of zeros.

Problems for oral practice:

1. 140 ÷ 7	**7.** 3600 ÷ 9
2. 240 ÷ 6	**8.** 2700 ÷ 3
3. 360 ÷ 9	**9.** 450 ÷ 5
4. 540 ÷ 6	**10.** 7700 ÷ 11
5. 720 ÷ 9	**11.** 4200 ÷ 7
6. 4800 ÷ 12	**12.** 9900 ÷ 11

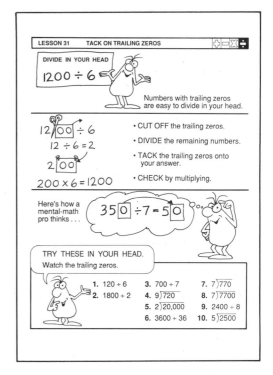

LESSON 32   CANCELING COMMON ZEROS
Mental math skill: Dividing when there are trailing zeros in both the divisor and dividend

Demonstrate that the division problem 4 ÷ 2 gives the same answer as 40 ÷ 20, 400 ÷ 200, 4000 ÷ 2000, and so forth. Students should recognize that "canceling common zeros" is the same as dividing both numbers by 10, or 100, or 1000, and so forth. Be sure students understand that they can cancel only *common* or *shared* trailing zeros. For example, even though both numbers in the problem 603 ÷ 30 have a zero, they are not *common* zeros, because they do not have the same place value. You may need to show several different examples to be sure students can identify division problems involving common zeros.

    For the first few TRY THESE problems, ask students how many zeros can be canceled. As with other mental division, students should check their answers by multiplying.

Problems for oral practice:
1. 300 ÷ 20
2. 400 ÷ 50
3. 500 ÷ 10
4. 1000 ÷ 20
5. 1200 ÷ 40
6. 700 ÷ 70
7. 2400 ÷ 600
8. 3600 ÷ 40
9. 5400 ÷ 60
10. 7200 ÷ 800
11. 450 ÷ 50
12. 6300 ÷ 700

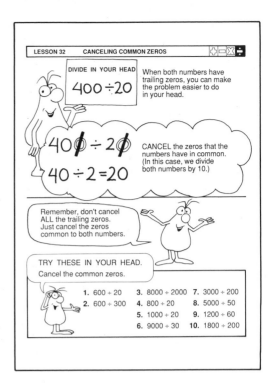

LESSON 33   BREAKING UP THE DIVIDEND
Mental math skill: Dividing by expanding the dividend

This strategy is based on "left-to-right division," which is essentially the same way we approach division in written computation. Students will need to recognize that there is more than one way to expand the dividend, and that they need to choose the way that gives them compatible numbers (the easiest numbers to divide). For example, given the problem at the top of the transparency, we *could* break up 126 into 100 and 26. However, since neither of those numbers can be evenly divided by 3, there is no reason to use them; breaking it into 120 and 6 clearly makes more sense.

    For the first few TRY THESE problems, ask students to tell different ways to break up the dividend and decide which way is best for a given problem. As before, encourage students to check division answers by multiplying.

Problems for oral practice:
1. 128 ÷ 4
2. 248 ÷ 4
3. 124 ÷ 4
4. 306 ÷ 3
5. 159 ÷ 3
6. 123 ÷ 3
7. 155 ÷ 5
8. 250 ÷ 5
9. 355 ÷ 5
10. 246 ÷ 6
11. 366 ÷ 6
12. 488 ÷ 8

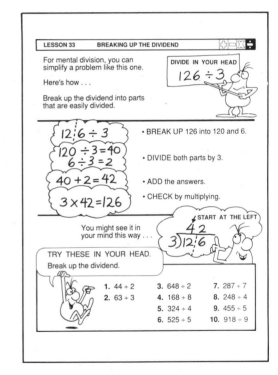

LESSON 34   THINK MONEY
Mental math skill: Multiplying any number by 5, 25, or 50

This strategy relies on students' familiarity with money amounts to help them with mental multiplication. It is a strategy that will increase in power over the years as students become even more comfortable at working with money.

You can warm up for the lesson with questions like these: "How many quarters in 1 dollar? in 2 dollars? in 4 dollars? How many half dollars in 1 dollar? in 3 dollars? in 7 dollars?"

Be sure that students remember, when they "think money," to multiply their dime answers by 10 [cents] and their dollar answers by 100 [cents]. Alternatively, they might think of this step as "tacking on trailing zeros."

As you work through the TRY THESE problems, ask students to explain how "thinking money" works in the different situations.

Problems for oral practice:
1. 36 nickels = ?
2. 48 nickels = ?
3. 12 nickels = ?
4. 240 nickels = ?
5. 16 quarters = ?
6. 28 quarters = ?
7. 36 quarters = ?
8. 44 quarters = ?
9. 32 half dollars = ?
10. 52 half dollars = ?
11. 64 half dollars = ?
12. 58 half dollars = ?

LESSON 35 SEARCHING FOR COMPATIBLES
Mental math skill: Using compatible numbers to simplify multi-step multiplication

The trick to this strategy is recognizing which numbers in a problem are compatible. In multiplication, "compatible" numbers are those that yield a product that's easy to work with—usually a multiple of ten, such as 10, 20, 50, 100, 200, and so forth. Sometimes there will be several different ways of combining factors. For example, look at the problem on the transparency. Rather than combining 2×5 and 2×5 to get 10×10 or 100, we might combine 5×5 to make 25, and 2×2 to make 4, then 4×25 to get 100. The result is exactly the same; we just got there with different compatible pairs.

In the TRY THESE problems, help students find the combinations that work best for mental multiplication. That is, in problem number 2, we *could* combine 2×11 to get 22, but that doesn't do us much good because 22×15 is not especially easy to compute mentally. Instead we combine 2×15 to get 30, because 30×11 *is* easy to compute in our heads.

You might alert students to one possible danger in using this strategy: in combining and rearranging, it can be easy to omit one of the factors inadvertently. We should always double-check to be sure this hasn't happened.

Problems for oral practice: The strategy presented in this lesson does not lend itself to oral practice; students need to be able to see all the factors at once to locate compatibles.

LESSON 36 MAKE-YOUR-OWN COMPATIBLE FACTORS

Mental math skill: Factoring and rearranging to simplify multiplication problems

To make the best use of this strategy, students may need practice in factoring. Ask them to name the factors of 25... of 32... of 36...of 27...of 48. For the first few TRY THESE problems, help students decide which factors will give them the best compatible pairs. Encourage alternative solutions, reminding students that there is no single "right" way. Whichever numbers are easiest for them to multiply mentally are "right" for them.

Problems for oral practice: As in the preceding lesson, this strategy does not lend itself to oral practice; most students will need to see the numbers that they are factoring and rearranging in their heads.

LESSON 36   MAKE-YOUR-OWN COMPATIBLE FACTORS

Here's a trick that can simplify mental multiplication . . .

24×25

Rearrange one or both of the numbers.

Your aim is to find compatible pairs.

24×25

$6 \times 4 \times 25$

$6 \times \boxed{4} \times \boxed{25}$ COMPATIBLE!

$6 \times 100 = 600$

Can you find a different way to rearrange 24×25?

TRY THESE IN YOUR HEAD.
Rearrange to find compatible pairs.

1. 8×15 3. 15×16 7. 12×15
2. 15×24 4. 36×50 8. 18×500
5. 48×15 9. 12×35
6. 24×500 10. 15×26

UNIT FOUR REVIEW

To prepare students for the Unit Four progress test, help them review the mental math strategies presented in lessons 28–36. Go over the mental math techniques listed in the box at left, working through the sample problems together. In the numbered review exercises, encourage discussion of different strategies that could be used for the same problem.

Students will need to pick up speed with the new strategies if they are to succeed on the timed test. Plan to give them some timed practice with problems you select at random from the Power Builder sets for lessons 28–36. You can present these orally or write them on the board, erasing them after a set length of time. Gradually shorten the time you allow for selecting a strategy and computing the answer.

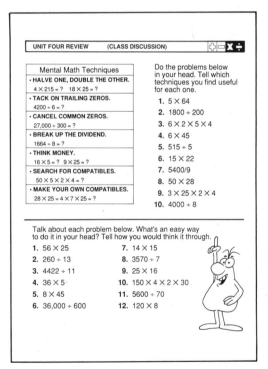

UNIT FOUR REVIEW   (CLASS DISCUSSION)

Mental Math Techniques
• HALVE ONE, DOUBLE THE OTHER.
$4 \times 215 = ?$ $18 \times 25 = ?$
• TACK ON TRAILING ZEROS.
$4200 \div 6 = ?$
• CANCEL COMMON ZEROS.
$27,000 \div 300 = ?$
• BREAK UP THE DIVIDEND.
$1664 \div 8 = ?$
• THINK MONEY.
$16 \times 5 = ?$ $9 \times 25 = ?$
• SEARCH FOR COMPATIBLES.
$50 \times 5 \times 2 \times 4 = ?$
• MAKE YOUR OWN COMPATIBLES.
$28 \times 25 = 4 \times 7 \times 25 = ?$

Do the problems below in your head. Tell which techniques you find useful for each one.

1. 5×64
2. $1800 \div 200$
3. $6 \times 2 \times 5 \times 4$
4. 6×45
5. $515 \div 5$
6. 15×22
7. $5400/9$
8. 50×28
9. $3 \times 25 \times 2 \times 4$
10. $4000 \div 8$

Talk about each problem below. What's an easy way to do it in your head? Tell how you would think it through.

1. 56×25 7. 14×15
2. $260 \div 13$ 8. $3570 \div 7$
3. $4422 \div 11$ 9. 25×16
4. 36×5 10. $150 \times 4 \times 2 \times 30$
5. 8×45 11. $5600 \div 70$
6. $36,000 \div 600$ 12. 120×8

The Memory of a Mentalmathlete

In order to do a difficult mental calculation, you have to remember lots of numbers. Most MENTALMATHLETES have excellent memories, especially for numbers. How's YOUR number memory?

Study this number series for five seconds and then try to write it down in the correct order.

6 2 1 3 1 7

Did you remember it? Now try again with this number series.

7 4 3 9 1 5 8 7 2 8

How well did you do this time?

Study this next number series, then try to write it down **backwards.**

2 1 8 4 7 5

Did you find it more difficult to remember numbers backwards than forwards?

MENTALMATHLETE Salo Finkelstein would find these memory tests very easy. He once correctly repeated the following series both forwards and backwards after viewing it for only **one** second!

4 8 6 3 5 7 4 9 8 7 3 9 8 6 4 8 1 0 3 5 9 2 5 4 6 9

The average person can memorize and repeat 6 or 7 numbers forwards and 5 or 6 numbers backwards. What about YOU?

The Memory of a Mental Mathlete

The number-memory tests on this "Mentalmathletes" page are best presented on an overhead projector after you have masked all four series of numbers. To test students' memory, expose each of the first three series in turn for five seconds, then recover it. Ask students to write down the series as they remember it.

To illustrate Mentalmathlete Finkelstein's phenomenal ability, expose the last number series for only **one** second. Then expose it for **ten** seconds and challenge students to write down as much of it as they can recall.

You can have some fun with this page, discovering which students in class can remember the most numbers forwards and the most numbers backwards as you give them longer and longer series of random digits. Name the winners "Mentalmathletes" for the day.

Discuss with students the types of numbers we have to remember in daily life, and their typical length; for example: street addresses, telephone numbers, social security numbers.

How do you do a math problem?

With paper and pencil?

Often it's faster and easier to do it in your head!

500 + 300 + 40

840

Try this one in your head.
Take it one step at a time.

400 + 200 + 50

4 hundred plus 2 hundred is 6 hundred, plus 50 is 650.

The key is doing one step at a time. That way you have only one number to keep in your head.

TRY THESE IN YOUR HEAD.

Do one step at a time.

1. 300 + 200 + 40
2. 600 + 100 + 20
3. 500 + 30 + 400
4. 7000 + 2000 + 500

5. 4000 + 5000 + 400
6. 6000 + 100 + 2000
7. 700 + 4000 + 300
8. 500 + 20 + 3000
9. 50 + 400 + 30 + 5000
10. 400 + 2000 + 60 + 500

POWER BUILDER A

1. 200 + 300 = _500_

2. 500 + 400 = _900_

3. 600 + 500 = _1000_

4. 700 + 800 = _____

5. 300 + 200 + 500 = _700_

6. 200 + 100 + 400 = _700_

7. 700 + 300 + 200 = _1,700_

8. 100 + 500 + 600 = _____

9. 3000 + 4000 + 1000 = _____

10. 7000 + 3000 + 2000 = _____

11. 200 + 400 + 50 = _____

12. 300 + 700 + 20 = _____

13. 500 + 300 + 70 = _____

14. 400 + 50 + 300 = _____

15. 100 + 30 + 600 = _____

16. 5000 + 400 + 2000 = _____

17. 7000 + 300 + 200 = _____

18. 4000 + 300 + 1000 = _____

19. 700 + 3000 + 50 = _____

20. 4000 + 2000 + 50 + 40 = _____

THINK IT THROUGH

I have four coins in my pocket. Together they are worth 80 cents. What coins do I have?

POWER BUILDER B

1. 200 + 600 + 50 = _850_

2. 300 + 800 + 90 = _____

3. 30 + 700 + 500 = _____

4. 50 + 800 + 400 = _____

5. 700 + 100 + 90 = _____

6. 900 + 40 + 500 = _____

7. 600 + 800 + 20 = _____

8. 300 + 70 + 500 = _____

9. 700 + 600 + 50 + 40 = _____

10. 800 + 700 + 30 + 20 = _____

11. 300 + 7000 + 50 = _4050_

12. 1000 + 90 + 500 = _1590_

13. 800 + 70 + 5000 = _5870_

14. 4000 + 600 + 6000 = _10,600_

15. 900 + 80 + 2000 = _____

16. 300 + 7000 + 400 + 50 = _____

17. 200 + 80 + 8000 = _____

18. 100 + 50 + 4000 + 2000 = _____

19. 6000 + 400 + 300 + 2000 = _____

20. 5000 + 20 + 2000 + 100 = _____

THINK IT THROUGH

I have five coins in my pocket. Together they are worth 55 cents. What coins do I have?

Place value names can help you keep track when you add in your head.

$500 + 310$

5 **hundred** plus 3 **hundred** 10 is 8 **hundred** 10.

Be sure to add digits with the same place value!

$430 + 500$

$430 + 500$

9 hundred 30, or 930

$5200 + 400$

$5200 + 400$

5 thousand 6 hundred, or 5600

TRY THESE IN YOUR HEAD.

Use place value names.

1. 340 + 600	**3.** 630 + 700	**7.** 3200 + 700
2. 280 + 500	**4.** 700 + 360	**8.** 400 + 3500
	5. 800 + 240	**9.** 200 + 7600
	6. 2400 + 500	**10.** 4100 + 400

POWER BUILDER A

1. 540 + 200 = _____
2. 170 + 400 = _____
3. 420 + 300 = _____
4. 500 + 430 = _____
5. 600 + 250 = _____
6. 200 + 720 = _____
7. 400 + 850 = _____
8. 600 + 740 = _____
9. 930 + 500 = _____
10. 870 + 300 = _____

11. 800 + 870 = _____
12. 600 + 990 = _____
13. 230 + 800 = _____
14. 890 + 400 = _____
15. 660 + 600 = _____
16. 500 + 550 = _____
17. 2600 + 300 = _____
18. 8100 + 500 = _____
19. 600 + 3300 = _____
20. 4200 + 500 = _____

THINK IT THROUGH

What is the sum of the largest three-digit number and the smallest two-digit number?

POWER BUILDER B

1. 350 + 200 = _____
2. 190 + 500 = _____
3. 720 + 100 = _____
4. 460 + 400 = _____
5. 800 + 180 = _____
6. 300 + 350 = _____
7. 500 + 720 = _____
8. 950 + 400 = _____
9. 780 + 800 = _____
10. 750 + 300 = _____

11. 950 + 900 = _____
12. 300 + 770 = _____
13. 490 + 700 = _____
14. 650 + 600 = _____
15. 750 + 700 = _____
16. 820 + 900 = _____
17. 3100 + 700 = _____
18. 200 + 4500 = _____
19. 800 + 6100 = _____
20. 3300 + 400 = _____

THINK IT THROUGH

What is the sum of the smallest three-digit number and the smallest four-digit number?

Knowing one basic addition fact can help you add other problems in your head.

For example . . .   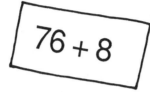 $6 + 8 = 14$

That fact can help you add these:

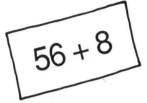 $56 + 8$ $76 + 8$ $136 + 8$

How?   Look at the endings:

$$56 + 8 \text{ is } 50 + 14 \text{ or } 64$$
$$76 + 8 \text{ is } 70 + 14 \text{ or } 84$$
$$136 + 8 \text{ is } 130 + 14 \text{ or } 144$$

It works when there are zeros, too.

$$560 + 80 \text{ is } 500 + 140 \text{ or } 640$$
$$760 + 80 \text{ is } 700 + 140 \text{ or } 840$$

TRY THESE IN YOUR HEAD.

Use what you know!

1. $47 + 5$ 3. $137 + 5$ 6. $48 + 9$
2. $87 + 5$ 4. $470 + 50$ 7. $78 + 9$
                  5. $770 + 50$ 8. $138 + 9$
                                    9. $380 + 90$
                                    10. $580 + 90$

POWER BUILDER A

1. $8 + 5 =$ _____
2. $28 + 5 =$ _____
3. $338 + 5 =$ _____
4. $80 + 50 =$ _____
5. $480 + 50 =$ _____
6. $7 + 4 =$ _____
7. $47 + 4 =$ _____
8. $847 + 4 =$ _____
9. $8 + 7 =$ _____
10. $58 + 7 =$ _____

11. $6 + 9 =$ _____
12. $56 + 9 =$ _____
13. $456 + 9 =$ _____
14. $560 + 90 =$ _____
15. $260 + 90 =$ _____
16. $7 + 8 =$ _____
17. $47 + 8 =$ _____
18. $647 + 8 =$ _____
19. $470 + 80 =$ _____
20. $170 + 80 =$ _____

THINK IT THROUGH

If the day after tomorrow is the day before Saturday, what day is today?

POWER BUILDER B

1. $7 + 6 =$ _____
2. $17 + 6 =$ _____
3. $327 + 6 =$ _____
4. $70 + 60 =$ _____
5. $470 + 60 =$ _____
6. $5 + 8 =$ _____
7. $35 + 8 =$ _____
8. $285 + 8 =$ _____
9. $470 + 80 =$ _____
10. $170 + 80 =$ _____

11. $9 + 4 =$ _____
12. $39 + 4 =$ _____
13. $279 + 4 =$ _____
14. $190 + 40 =$ _____
15. $890 + 40 =$ _____
16. $6 + 5 =$ _____
17. $36 + 5 =$ _____
18. $146 + 5 =$ _____
19. $360 + 50 =$ _____
20. $860 + 50 =$ _____

THINK IT THROUGH

If a week from tomorrow is Wednesday, what day was yesterday?

Here's one way to add in your head.

Break up one of the numbers and add the parts, one step at a time. Like this . . .

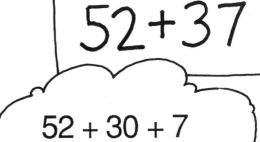

$52 + 37$

$52 + 30 + 7$

. . . 82 . . . 89

Try this one.
Break up 260.

$524 + 260$

$524 + 200 + 60$

. . . 724 . . . 784

TRY THESE IN YOUR HEAD.

Break up one of the numbers.

1. 48 + 21	**3.** 34 + 52	**7.** 400 + 231	
2. 53 + 34	**4.** 456 + 120	**8.** 456 + 42	
	5. 438 + 340	**9.** 381 + 405	
	6. 629 + 310	**10.** 705 + 220	

POWER BUILDER A

1. 247 + 130 = _____

2. 575 + 203 = _____

3. 839 + 140 = _____

4. 153 + 530 = _____

5. 609 + 180 = _____

6. 545 + 320 = _____

7. 258 + 320 = _____

8. 675 + 120 = _____

9. 431 + 506 = _____

10. 274 + 310 = _____

11. 205 + 831 = _____

12. 335 + 450 = _____

13. 453 + 502 = _____

14. 426 + 403 = _____

15. 220 + 354 = _____

16. 514 + 405 = _____

17. 328 + 550 = _____

18. 805 + 172 = _____

19. 506 + 340 = _____

20. 263 + 420 = _____

THINK IT THROUGH

If June 13 is the second Thursday of the month, what is the date of the first Tuesday in June?

POWER BUILDER B

1. 315 + 210 = _____

2. 465 + 301 = _____

3. 746 + 150 = _____

4. 241 + 530 = _____

5. 508 + 260 = _____

6. 412 + 530 = _____

7. 627 + 370 = _____

8. 542 + 305 = _____

9. 418 + 410 = _____

10. 516 + 202 = _____

11. 104 + 625 = _____

12. 455 + 220 = _____

13. 856 + 102 = _____

14. 169 + 530 = _____

15. 428 + 460 = _____

16. 314 + 504 = _____

17. 256 + 220 = _____

18. 724 + 203 = _____

19. 603 + 280 = _____

20. 149 + 550 = _____

THINK IT THROUGH

If October 25 is the last Friday of the month, what day of the week is October 1?

ADD IN YOUR HEAD

$$28 + 17$$

That's too hard!
I need a pencil!

You don't need a pencil.
It's easy in your head.

Break up one of the numbers and
add the parts, one step at a time.

28 plus 10 is 38,
plus 7 is 45.

Where did the 10 and
the 7 come from?

TRY THESE IN YOUR HEAD.

Break up one of the numbers.

1. 29 + 14	**3.** 35 + 47	**7.** 28 + 25
2. 53 + 28	**4.** 45 + 36	**8.** 29 + 44
	5. 65 + 27	**9.** 48 + 33
	6. 58 + 24	**10.** 56 + 35

POWER BUILDER A

1. 39 + 15 = _____
2. 48 + 25 = _____
3. 68 + 105 = _____
4. 38 + 204 = _____
5. 67 + 204 = _____
6. 35 + 38 = _____
7. 48 + 25 = _____
8. 65 + 26 = _____
9. 38 + 27 = _____
10. 53 + 19 = _____

11. 28 + 27 = _____
12. 16 + 26 = _____
13. 45 + 28 = _____
14. 58 + 17 = _____
15. 39 + 24 = _____
16. 53 + 29 = _____
17. 18 + 17 = _____
18. 45 + 48 = _____
19. 36 + 48 = _____
20. 28 + 18 = _____

THINK IT THROUGH

The sum of the ages of a mother, a father, and their son is 100 years. Each of their ages is a multiple of 10, and the mother was 30 years old when her son was born. How old is the son?

POWER BUILDER B

1. 26 + 19 = _____
2. 49 + 263 = _____
3. 28 + 24 = _____
4. 67 + 15 = _____
5. 78 + 175 = _____
6. 54 + 28 = _____
7. 28 + 304 = _____
8. 65 + 26 = _____
9. 77 + 15 = _____
10. 48 + 17 = _____

11. 58 + 24 = _____
12. 33 + 18 = _____
13. 45 + 37 = _____
14. 54 + 28 = _____
15. 33 + 18 = _____
16. 63 + 28 = _____
17. 27 + 55 = _____
18. 38 + 45 = _____
19. 28 + 49 = _____
20. 36 + 47 = _____

THINK IT THROUGH

A woman's age is her husband's age with the digits reversed. The man is older. If the sum of their ages is 99 and the difference is 9, how old is each?

SUBTRACT IN YOUR HEAD | $7000 - 400$

Notice that these numbers share two common zeros.

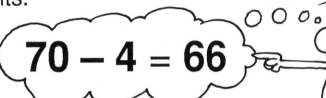

$70\,00 - 4\,00$

Drop those zeros for now and focus on the front-end digits.

$70 - 4 = 66$

But don't forget those two zeros! Put them back to get the right place value.

$66\,00$

66 hundred

TRY THESE IN YOUR HEAD. Drop common zeros . . . but then put them back.

1. $700 - 300$
2. $8000 - 4000$
3. $17,000 - 5,000$
4. $4000 - 600$
5. $3000 - 500$

6. $4900 - 700$
7. $5000 - 200 - 100$
8. $3800 - 300 - 200$
9. $9600 - 7000 - 500$
10. $8000 - 3000 - 600$

POWER BUILDER A

1. 800 − 500 = _____

2. 900 − 200 = _____

3. 1200 − 700 = _____

4. 1500 − 900 = _____

5. 4000 − 1000 = _____

6. 8000 − 6000 = _____

7. 13,000 − 8,000 = _____

8. 17,000 − 9,000 = _____

9. 5000 − 100 = _____

10. 8000 − 500 = _____

11. 7000 − 700 = _____

12. 4000 − 4000 = _____

13. 6000 − 800 = _____

14. 1900 − 700 = _____

15. 1000 − 500 − 400 = _____

16. 10,000 − 5,000 − 4,000 = _____

17. 1800 − 900 − 500 = _____

18. 2000 − 500 − 300 = _____

19. 8000 − 1000 − 100 = _____

20. 5000 − 2000 − 200 = _____

THINK IT THROUGH

Begin with 100. Subtract half of 60. Add half of 40. What do you get?

POWER BUILDER B

1. 700 − 300 = _____

2. 800 − 600 = _____

3. 1100 − 500 = _____

4. 1600 − 800 = _____

5. 5000 − 2000 = _____

6. 7000 − 4000 = _____

7. 14,000 − 8,000 = _____

8. 15,000 − 9,000 = _____

9. 3000 − 100 = _____

10. 5000 − 500 = _____

11. 6000 − 600 = _____

12. 3000 − 3000 = _____

13. 7000 − 900 = _____

14. 1400 − 300 = _____

15. 1200 − 500 − 500 = _____

16. 10,000 − 5,000 − 3,000 = _____

17. 2000 − 600 − 900 = _____

18. 5000 − 700 − 100 = _____

19. 9000 − 5000 − 500 = _____

20. 4000 − 3000 − 300 = _____

THINK IT THROUGH

Begin with 100. Add half of 100. Subtract half of 20. What do you get?

SUBTRACT IN
YOUR HEAD

$$90 - 50$$

When the numbers end in zero, use a shortcut.

Drop the common zeros.

$9 - 5 = 4 \ldots$
so it's 40.

Sometimes there are different shortcuts for the same problem.

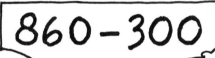

$$860 - 300$$

$86 - 30 = 56$
with one zero,
or 560.

$8 - 3 = 5$
That's 500 with
60 more, or 560.

Both shortcuts work.
Which do you like better?

TRY THESE IN YOUR HEAD.

What shortcut will you use?

1. 80 − 30	**3.** 1400 − 500	**7.** 850 − 30
2. 800 − 600	**4.** 680 − 200	**8.** 1680 − 20
	5. 940 − 700	**9.** 2470 − 300
	6. 590 − 300	**10.** 1230 − 200

POWER BUILDER A

1. 70 − 30 = _____
2. 600 − 200 = _____
3. 1500 − 900 = _____
4. 830 − 200 = _____
5. 180 − 90 = _____
6. 130 − 70 = _____
7. 250 − 100 = _____
8. 440 − 300 = _____
9. 1850 − 30 = _____
10. 2900 − 300 = _____

11. 120 − 70 = _____
12. 150 − 90 = _____
13. 780 − 400 = _____
14. 1600 − 700 = _____
15. 170 − 80 = _____
16. 120 − 60 = _____
17. 350 − 100 = _____
18. 530 − 200 = _____
19. 1450 − 40 = _____
20. 3400 − 400 = _____

THINK IT THROUGH

Begin with 5 hundreds. Subtract 3 hundreds. Subtract 4 tens. Subtract 6 ones. What is left?

POWER BUILDER B

1. 90 − 30 = _____
2. 150 − 80 = _____
3. 800 − 500 = _____
4. 1400 − 600 = _____
5. 110 − 50 = _____
6. 540 − 200 = _____
7. 480 − 100 = _____
8. 620 − 600 = _____
9. 250 − 40 = _____
10. 1900 − 500 = _____

11. 320 − 50 = _____
12. 130 − 80 = _____
13. 1300 − 900 = _____
14. 450 − 300 = _____
15. 270 − 60 = _____
16. 1520 − 500 = _____
17. 2500 − 800 = _____
18. 1680 − 70 = _____
19. 3820 − 600 = _____
20. 450 − 400 = _____

THINK IT THROUGH

Begin with 12 hundreds. Subtract 3 hundreds. Subtract 7 tens. Subtract 4 ones. What is left?

Some subtraction problems are easier than others.

NOT SO EASY

$436 - 197$

$$-\dfrac{348}{289}$$

EASIER

$376 - 156$

$$-\dfrac{273}{143}$$

What makes these easier?

When the ending digits are the same, try this . . .

• Subtract the front-end digits.

• Then fix the place value.

$376 - 56$

$37 - 5 = 32$

It's 32 tens, or 320.

TRY THESE IN YOUR HEAD.
Focus on the front end.
Then fix the place value.

1. $56 - 6$ **3.** $84 - 24$ **7.** $638 - 138$

2. $29 - 9$ **4.** $38 - 28$ **8.** $371 - 51$

                    5. $319 - 9$ **9.** $592 - 192$

                    6. $253 - 43$ **10.** $729 - 209$

POWER BUILDER A

1. 35 − 5 = _____

2. 48 − 8 = _____

3. 73 − 23 = _____

4. 56 − 16 = _____

5. 82 − 2 = _____

6. 37 − 27 = _____

7. 75 − 25 = _____

8. 52 − 52 = _____

9. 48 − 28 = _____

10. 90 − 30 = _____

11. 152 − 2 = _____

12. 345 − 45 = _____

13. 224 − 24 = _____

14. 175 − 75 = _____

15. 411 − 11 = _____

16. 382 − 52 = _____

17. 241 − 21 = _____

18. 428 − 208 = _____

19. 517 − 117 = _____

20. 635 − 435 = _____

THINK IT THROUGH

Subtract the fifth odd number from the tenth odd number. What is the difference?

POWER BUILDER B

1. 26 − 6 = _____

2. 52 − 2 = _____

3. 89 − 19 = _____

4. 45 − 15 = _____

5. 98 − 8 = _____

6. 64 − 54 = _____

7. 43 − 43 = _____

8. 75 − 25 = _____

9. 68 − 28 = _____

10. 80 − 20 = _____

11. 227 − 7 = _____

12. 133 − 33 = _____

13. 345 − 45 = _____

14. 875 − 75 = _____

15. 619 − 19 = _____

16. 275 − 25 = _____

17. 543 − 13 = _____

18. 645 − 205 = _____

19. 275 − 175 = _____

20. 893 − 393 = _____

THINK IT THROUGH

If the sum of the first 437 counting numbers is subtracted from the sum of the first 438 counting numbers, what is the difference?

$$30 + 40 - 50 + 70$$

Yes, chains of numbers **look** hard.
But it's easy to do them
in your head.
What's the secret?

Psst . . . Do one step at a time!

Think in steps.

$$30 + 40 - 50 + 70$$

That's 70 . . . minus 50 . . .

is 20 . . . plus 70 . . .

is 90.

Here's another way
to think of it.

$$30 \quad + \quad 40 \quad - \quad 50 \quad + \quad 70$$

$$70 \quad - \quad 50$$

$$20 \quad + \quad 70$$

$$90$$

TRY THESE IN YOUR HEAD.

Do them one step at a time.

1. $20 + 60 - 30 - 10$
2. $80 - 50 + 30 + 10$
3. $60 + 30 - 40 - 40$
4. $90 - 40 + 30 - 10 - 20$
5. $80 - 50 + 30 - 20 + 10$

6. $60 + 20 - 40 - 30 + 20$
7. $50 + 10 + 20 - 30 + 20 - 30$
8. $70 - 30 + 50 - 30 + 40 + 80$
9. $30 + 20 + 30 - 50 - 10 + 60$
10. $50 + 30 - 40 - 10 + 20 + 70$

POWER BUILDER A

1. 40 + 20 − 30 = _____

2. 50 + 30 − 40 + 10 = _____

3. 70 − 50 + 50 − 20 = _____

4. 10 + 20 + 30 − 40 = _____

5. 40 + 50 − 60 + 20 = _____

6. 50 + 20 − 40 − 20 = _____

7. 70 + 20 − 80 + 20 = _____

8. 90 + 80 − 90 + 20 = _____

9. 10 + 80 − 90 + 20 = _____

10. 20 + 20 + 20 + 20 + 10 = _____

11. 50 + 30 − 20 = _____

12. 40 + 40 − 50 = _____

13. 70 − 50 + 50 − 20 = _____

14. 80 − 10 − 20 − 30 = _____

15. 70 − 70 + 30 − 20 = _____

16. 20 + 30 + 40 − 50 = _____

17. 40 + 40 − 40 − 40 = _____

18. 20 + 70 − 30 − 30 = _____

19. 10 + 50 + 20 − 70 = _____

20. 20 + 10 + 20 + 20 + 20 = _____

THINK IT THROUGH

Find the sum of all multiples of 10 less than 100.

POWER BUILDER B

1. 30 + 20 + 40 = _____

2. 20 + 30 − 40 + 50 = _____

3. 70 − 10 − 20 − 30 = _____

4. 50 + 40 − 60 + 20 = _____

5. 70 + 10 − 20 − 30 = _____

6. 60 + 30 − 40 − 20 = _____

7. 80 − 80 + 20 + 50 = _____

8. 70 + 20 − 50 + 30 = _____

9. 40 + 30 + 20 − 10 = _____

10. 80 + 10 − 20 − 30 = _____

11. 50 + 30 − 40 = _____

12. 70 + 20 − 40 − 40 = _____

13. 40 + 20 − 50 + 30 = _____

14. 70 + 20 − 20 + 10 = _____

15. 40 + 50 − 50 + 30 = _____

16. 70 + 20 − 30 − 30 = _____

17. 20 + 20 + 20 + 20 − 10 = _____

18. 90 − 80 + 70 − 60 = _____

19. 40 − 30 + 20 − 10 = _____

20. 90 − 20 − 30 − 40 = _____

THINK IT THROUGH

Find the sum of all multiples of 100 less than 1000.

Mental Math Techniques
• **TAKE IT ONE STEP AT A TIME.** $60 + 20 - 10 + 30 - 50 = ?$
• **USE PLACE VALUE NAMES.** $1200 + 370 + 400 = ?$
• **USE WHAT YOU KNOW.** $9 + 7 = 16$, so $89 + 7 = ?$
• **BREAK IT UP.** $62 + 27 = 62 + 20 + 7 = ?$
• **DROP COMMON ZEROS.** $2700 - 300 = ?$
• **FOCUS ON THE FRONT END.** $4396 - 196 = ?$

Do the problems below in your head. Tell which techniques you find useful for each one.

1. $1720 + 400$
2. $870 - 20$
3. $47 + 33$
4. $378 - 58$
5. $1400 + 250 + 300$
6. $124 + 8$
7. $4000 - 600$
8. $27 + 19$
9. $1740 - 340$
10. $80 + 10 - 30 + 40 - 70$

Talk about each problem below. What's an easy way to do it in your head? Tell how you would think it through.

1. $66 + 7$
2. $40 - 20 + 70 - 10 - 50$
3. $413 - 203$
4. $150 - 70$
5. $520 + 1200 + 6000$
6. $73 + 26$
7. $2500 - 300$
8. $580 + 40$
9. $600 - 400 + 50 + 100$
10. $177 + 34$
11. $500 + 3200 + 70$
12. $164 - 44$

1. $400 + 30 + 300 =$ _____

2. $800 + 240 =$ _____

3. $48 + 17 =$ _____

4. $2000 + 700 + 300 + 600 =$ _____

5. $63 + 25 =$ _____

6. $700 - 200 =$ _____

7. $70 - 60 + 40 + 30 - 20 =$ _____

8. $570 - 40 =$ _____

9. $85 + 8 =$ _____

10. $940 - 300 =$ _____

11. $51 + 37 =$ _____

12. $329 - 9 =$ _____

13. $850 + 80 =$ _____

14. $3000 - 700 =$ _____

15. $28 + 15 =$ _____

16. $60 + 400 + 20 + 5000 =$ _____

17. $820 - 500 =$ _____

18. $3300 + 500 =$ _____

19. $84 - 24 =$ _____

20. $452 + 36 =$ _____

21. $420 + 1300 =$ _____

22. $80 + 10 - 70 + 40 =$ _____

23. $9000 - 2000 - 500 =$ _____

24. $528 + 140 =$ _____

25. $3450 - 1050 =$ _____

26. $645 - 35 =$ _____

27. $55 + 29 =$ _____

28. $6500 - 200 - 3000 =$ _____

29. $351 - 31 =$ _____

30. $4870 - 500 =$ _____

31. $90 - 20 - 30 - 20 + 50 =$ _____

32. $1450 + 300 =$ _____

33. $66 + 19 =$ _____

34. $45 + 22 =$ _____

35. $59 + 25 =$ _____

36. $2850 - 700 =$ _____

37. $4768 - 3068 =$ _____

38. $575 + 12 =$ _____

39. $850 - 150 =$ _____

40. $55 + 27 =$ _____

Doing Several Things at Once

Have you ever tried to do several things at one time? What usually happens? Let's see how you do . . .

1. Add these numbers in your head while softly clapping your hands in a regular beat.

$$6 + 1 + 2 + 3 + 2 + 3 + 1$$

2. Add these next numbers in your head while quietly singing the national anthem to yourself.

$$2 + 3 + 1 + 6 + 1 + 2 + 3$$

3. Now add these numbers in your head while quietly counting to yourself, starting with one.

$$3 + 2 + 1 + 5 + 2 + 3 + 2$$

Which task was the most difficult for you?

MENTALMATHLETE Maurice Dagbert could do tasks like this with ease. He was once given more than twenty difficult calculations (such as 12,475 × 48,326) to do in his head while he was playing the violin. When Dagbert completed the musical piece, he wrote down the results of his calculations—and they were all correct!

$$12{,}475 \times 48{,}326 = 602{,}866{,}850$$

Doing Several Things at Once

Like patting your head and rubbing your stomach at the same time, trying to do mental calculation while the brain is otherwise occupied can be surprisingly difficult—but it can be lots of fun to try! Present these tasks one at a time, giving the students ample time for each. You can present the calculation problems either visually (as shown on the page) or orally.

Ask students which task they found most difficult, and **why** it was difficult. (The third task, adding while counting, should prove to be the most difficult because the students need to keep two number patterns in their heads at the same time.)

When you add with pencil and paper, you usually start at the **right** and work toward the left.

To add in your head, try starting at the **left.**

THINK . . .

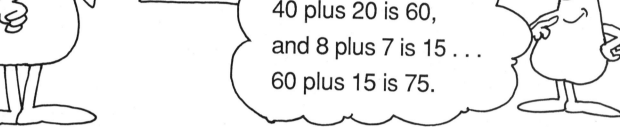

40 plus 20 is 60,

and 8 plus 7 is 15 . . .

60 plus 15 is 75.

Try this one from the left.

55 + 28

50 + 20 is 70 . . .

5 + 8 is 13 . . .

70 + 13 is 83.

TRY THESE IN YOUR HEAD.

Start at the left and add.

1. 35 + 49	**3.** 26 + 47	**7.** 55 + 29
2. 53 + 28	**4.** 19 + 37	**8.** 44 + 27
	5. 15 + 65	**9.** 19 + 63
	6. 47 + 28	**10.** 36 + 49

POWER BUILDER A

1. 28 + 15 = _____

2. 47 + 25 = _____

3. 18 + 24 = _____

4. 65 + 25 = _____

5. 53 + 19 = _____

6. 45 + 27 = _____

7. 38 + 24 = _____

8. 43 + 38 = _____

9. 15 + 65 = _____

10. 29 + 45 = _____

11. 54 + 28 = _____

12. 25 + 18 = _____

13. 36 + 45 = _____

14. 19 + 65 = _____

15. 57 + 26 = _____

16. 17 + 35 = _____

17. 79 + 18 = _____

18. 54 + 29 = _____

19. 45 + 36 = _____

20. 28 + 27 = _____

THINK IT THROUGH

If this is not a leap year, what is the date of the 100th day of the year?

POWER BUILDER B

1. 24 + 19 = _____

2. 68 + 24 = _____

3. 19 + 18 = _____

4. 34 + 47 = _____

5. 65 + 15 = _____

6. 29 + 15 = _____

7. 17 + 25 = _____

8. 19 + 37 = _____

9. 48 + 15 = _____

10. 26 + 55 = _____

11. 35 + 18 = _____

12. 17 + 49 = _____

13. 45 + 47 = _____

14. 37 + 28 = _____

15. 16 + 35 = _____

16. 69 + 18 = _____

17. 15 + 49 = _____

18. 23 + 28 = _____

19. 35 + 47 = _____

20. 26 + 39 = _____

THINK IT THROUGH

If you think of January 1 as day 1 and December 31 as day 365 (it is not a leap year), what day is May 28?

Subtraction problems come in two styles . . .

THOSE THAT **NEED** REGROUPING	436 – 28 5227 – 2981	THOSE THAT **DON'T NEED** REGROUPING	436 – 23 5227 – 2125

When they don't need regrouping,
you can start at either end.

AT THE BACK END

$$\begin{array}{r} 5227 \\ -2125 \end{array}$$

2 . . . 0 . . .

1 . . . 3 . . .

that's 3102.

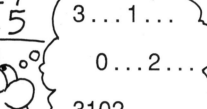

AT THE FRONT END

$$\begin{array}{r} 5227 \\ -2125 \end{array}$$

3 . . . 1 . . .

0 . . . 2 . . .

3102.

Starting at the front end makes
more sense because then you
don't have to juggle digits.

TRY THESE IN YOUR HEAD.

Start at the front end and subtract.

1. 47 – 26   3. 49 – 18   7. 5647 – 3515

2. 84 – 61   4. 357 – 135   8. 6892 – 1812

5. 846 – 715   9. 7368 – 4317

6. 947 – 645   10. 4807 – 1503

POWER BUILDER A

1. 99 − 35 = _____

2. 49 − 17 = _____

3. 58 − 24 = _____

4. 45 − 20 = _____

5. 67 − 33 = _____

6. 85 − 71 = _____

7. 156 − 50 = _____

8. 348 − 25 = _____

9. 265 − 54 = _____

10. 893 − 82 = _____

11. 475 − 150 = _____

12. 289 − 125 = _____

13. 850 − 130 = _____

14. 777 − 234 = _____

15. 594 − 203 = _____

16. 6517 − 2500 = _____

17. 8765 − 1234 = _____

18. 5029 − 4020 = _____

19. 6894 − 333 = _____

20. 9876 − 540 = _____

THINK IT THROUGH

The difference between two numbers is 10. If the numbers are doubled, what is the difference between them?

POWER BUILDER B

1. 99 − 54 = _____

2. 57 − 14 = _____

3. 37 − 23 = _____

4. 64 − 30 = _____

5. 47 − 22 = _____

6. 75 − 24 = _____

7. 185 − 40 = _____

8. 275 − 25 = _____

9. 486 − 75 = _____

10. 575 − 64 = _____

11. 365 − 125 = _____

12. 780 − 250 = _____

13. 984 − 430 = _____

14. 888 − 345 = _____

15. 687 − 505 = _____

16. 3527 − 1300 = _____

17. 6895 − 5050 = _____

18. 7533 − 1301 = _____

19. 7856 − 250 = _____

20. 9999 − 444 = _____

THINK IT THROUGH

The difference between two numbers is 25. If the numbers are doubled, what is the difference between them?

54

It's easy to add in your head when both numbers end in 5.

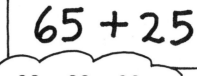

1. Add the tens.

2. Add the ones.

3. Find the total.

60 + 20 = 80

5 + 5 = 10

80 + 10 = 90

The answer will always end in zero!

Here's a trick to help add numbers in your head . . .

Expand to make them both end in 5 . . .
then add what's left over.

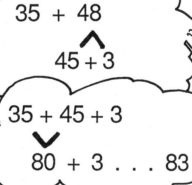

35 + 48

35 + 48
    ∧
  45 + 3

35 + 45 + 3
    ∨
80 + 3 83

TRY THESE IN YOUR HEAD.

Make both numbers end in 5.

1. 46 + 25	**3.** 55 + 27	**7.** 135 + 26
2. 17 + 45	**4.** 46 + 15	**8.** 145 + 19
	5. 39 + 85	**9.** 235 + 37
	6. 75 + 38	**10.** 55 + 38

MENTAL MATH IN THE MIDDLE GRADES
Copyright © 1987 by Dale Seymour Publications

POWER BUILDER A

1. 26 + 15 = _____

2. 45 + 29 = _____

3. 58 + 25 = _____

4. 66 + 25 = _____

5. 47 + 35 = _____

6. 75 + 17 = _____

7. 95 + 18 = _____

8. 88 + 15 = _____

9. 36 + 75 = _____

10. 65 + 67 = _____

11. 75 + 76 = _____

12. 125 + 26 = _____

13. 19 + 165 = _____

14. 245 + 56 = _____

15. 415 + 77 = _____

16. 255 + 49 = _____

17. 175 + 77 = _____

18. 455 + 26 = _____

19. 445 + 57 = _____

20. 418 + 55 = _____

THINK IT THROUGH

If you have 3 quarters and 10 nickels, and you spend 1 quarter and 7 nickels, how much money will you have left?

POWER BUILDER B

1. 35 + 17 = _____

2. 56 + 15 = _____

3. 77 + 15 = _____

4. 39 + 45 = _____

5. 55 + 28 = _____

6. 18 + 75 = _____

7. 85 + 26 = _____

8. 98 + 35 = _____

9. 75 + 46 = _____

10. 57 + 55 = _____

11. 78 + 75 = _____

12. 175 + 26 = _____

13. 17 + 135 = _____

14. 65 + 136 = _____

15. 75 + 217 = _____

16. 265 + 38 = _____

17. 175 + 76 = _____

18. 29 + 275 = _____

19. 525 + 77 = _____

20. 518 + 35 = _____

THINK IT THROUGH

If you have 5 quarters and 7 nickels, and you spend 3 nickels, how much money will you have left?

Find the pairs that total 10.

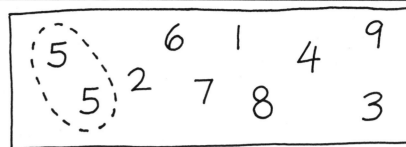

Tens are easy numbers to use.

You can "make tens" to make mental addition easier. Here's how . . .

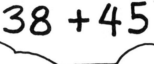

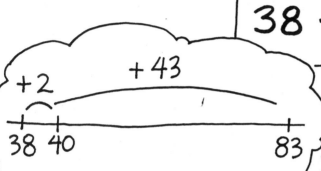

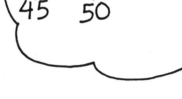

"Make tens" with 38, then adjust the 45.

Or "make tens" with 45, then adjust the 38.

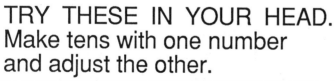

TRY THESE IN YOUR HEAD. Make tens with one number and adjust the other.

1. 49 + 23	**3.** 47 + 45	**7.** 54 + 39
2. 38 + 36	**4.** 27 + 39	**8.** 57 + 26
	5. 67 + 24	**9.** 28 + 46
	6. 38 + 57	**10.** 45 + 49

POWER BUILDER A

1. 49 + 13 = _____
2. 28 + 25 = _____
3. 39 + 45 = _____
4. 59 + 17 = _____
5. 58 + 14 = _____
6. 15 + 69 = _____
7. 24 + 38 = _____
8. 35 + 49 = _____
9. 43 + 18 = _____
10. 25 + 29 = _____

11. 48 + 49 = _____
12. 39 + 47 = _____
13. 58 + 18 = _____
14. 27 + 49 = _____
15. 38 + 39 = _____
16. 49 + 27 = _____
17. 69 + 18 = _____
18. 49 + 16 = _____
19. 18 + 79 = _____
20. 59 + 36 = _____

THINK IT THROUGH

Find the sum of the first ten even numbers (counting 0 as the first number). Look for a shortcut.

POWER BUILDER B

1. 48 + 14 = _____
2. 39 + 25 = _____
3. 29 + 33 = _____
4. 78 + 16 = _____
5. 58 + 15 = _____
6. 16 + 78 = _____
7. 25 + 39 = _____
8. 14 + 58 = _____
9. 26 + 68 = _____
10. 23 + 39 = _____

11. 39 + 38 = _____
12. 47 + 29 = _____
13. 19 + 65 = _____
14. 54 + 29 = _____
15. 49 + 47 = _____
16. 38 + 46 = _____
17. 79 + 18 = _____
18. 68 + 29 = _____
19. 39 + 47 = _____
20. 59 + 28 = _____

THINK IT THROUGH

Find the sum of the first ten odd numbers. Look for a shortcut.

$$\begin{array}{cc} 67 & 69 \\ -28 & -30 \end{array}$$

$$\begin{array}{cc} 43 & 48 \\ -15 & -20 \end{array}$$

$$\begin{array}{cc} 87 & 86 \\ -40 & -39 \end{array}$$

Which problem in each pair is easier?   Why?

$$\begin{array}{c} 55 \\ -28 \\ \hline \end{array}$$

"Making tens" can help you subtract in your head.

Adding 2 to 28 makes 30. That's easier to subtract. Then I'll adjust 55, too, to balance.

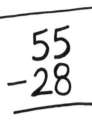

$$\begin{array}{rcl} 55 + 2 & \rightarrow & 57 \\ -28 + 2 & \rightarrow & -30 \\ \hline & & 27 \end{array}$$

Remember: Adding the same amount to both numbers leaves the difference unchanged!

TRY THESE IN YOUR HEAD.

Make tens and balance.

1. 83 −28	**3.** 72 −45	**5.** 70 − 23	**8.** 82 − 37
		6. 65 − 48	**9.** 75 − 27
2. 54 −39	**4.** 81 −54	**7.** 90 − 36	**10.** 93 − 39

POWER BUILDER A

1. 53 − 28 = _____

2. 44 − 19 = _____

3. 71 − 35 = _____

4. 85 − 29 = _____

5. 50 − 28 = _____

6. 45 − 17 = _____

7. 81 − 39 = _____

8. 56 − 37 = _____

9. 37 − 16 = _____

10. 42 − 28 = _____

11. 83 − 25 = _____

12. 46 − 29 = _____

13. 71 − 38 = _____

14. 82 − 26 = _____

15. 66 − 18 = _____

16. 80 − 29 = _____

17. 46 − 18 = _____

18. 94 − 49 = _____

19. 90 − 65 = _____

20. 73 − 56 = _____

THINK IT THROUGH

Subtract the largest two-digit even number from the largest three-digit even number.

POWER BUILDER B

1. 52 − 19 = _____

2. 83 − 28 = _____

3. 44 − 26 = _____

4. 55 − 17 = _____

5. 70 − 27 = _____

6. 51 − 29 = _____

7. 62 − 38 = _____

8. 71 − 19 = _____

9. 65 − 28 = _____

10. 82 − 66 = _____

11. 93 − 15 = _____

12. 66 − 39 = _____

13. 81 − 48 = _____

14. 92 − 35 = _____

15. 76 − 47 = _____

16. 70 − 28 = _____

17. 36 − 19 = _____

18. 84 − 36 = _____

19. 80 − 45 = _____

20. 83 − 49 = _____

THINK IT THROUGH

Subtract the smallest three-digit odd number from the smallest four-digit odd number.

Two numbers that total
a nice "tidy" sum (like 10,
or 100, or 1000) are called
compatible numbers.

45 and 55 are compatible.
So are 360 and 640.

Compatible numbers make mental math easy!
Learn to recognize them.

WE'RE COMPATIBLE!
TOGETHER WE MAKE 10.

Find compatible pairs.

4	60	40	71
56	75	29	30
44	33	12	67
96	70	88	25

Find compatible pairs.

400	300	550	600
510	620	250	100
630	900	700	380
450	750	490	370

TRY THESE. USE YOUR HEAD.

Think about compatible numbers.

1. On scrap paper, list
number pairs that
total 100. Write as
many as you can in
one minute.   GO!

2. How many different
pairs of numbers
total 1000?

POWER BUILDER A

1. $35 +$ _____ $= 100$

2. $94 +$ _____ $= 100$

3. $31 +$ _____ $= 100$

4. $46 +$ _____ $= 100$

5. $25 +$ _____ $= 100$

6. $100 - 17 =$ _____

7. $100 - 53 =$ _____

8. $100 - 62 =$ _____

9. $100 - 95 =$ _____

10. $100 - 39 =$ _____

11. $400 +$ _____ $= 1000$

12. $250 +$ _____ $= 1000$

13. $950 +$ _____ $= 1000$

14. $899 +$ _____ $= 1000$

15. $375 +$ _____ $= 1000$

16. $1000 - 501 =$ _____

17. $1000 - 695 =$ _____

18. $1000 - 99 =$ _____

19. $1000 - 725 =$ _____

20. $1000 - 645 =$ _____

THINK IT THROUGH

How many different pairs of whole numbers add to 100?

POWER BUILDER B

1. $50 +$ _____ $= 100$

2. $93 +$ _____ $= 100$

3. $49 +$ _____ $= 100$

4. $15 +$ _____ $= 100$

5. $33 +$ _____ $= 100$

6. $100 - 75 =$ _____

7. $100 - 8 =$ _____

8. $100 - 29 =$ _____

9. $100 - 80 =$ _____

10. $100 - 42 =$ _____

11. $700 +$ _____ $= 1000$

12. $975 +$ _____ $= 1000$

13. $499 +$ _____ $= 1000$

14. $450 +$ _____ $= 1000$

15. $95 +$ _____ $= 1000$

16. $1000 - 125 =$ _____

17. $1000 - 901 =$ _____

18. $1000 - 255 =$ _____

19. $1000 - 650 =$ _____

20. $1000 - 575 =$ _____

THINK IT THROUGH

How many different pairs of **even** whole numbers add to 100?

When you add compatible numbers, you get a "tidy" sum that is easy to use in your head.

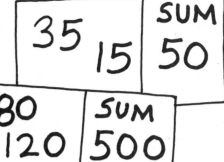

| 35 | 15 | SUM 50 |

| 75 | 125 | SUM | 200 | 140 | 160 | SUM | 300 | 380 | 120 | SUM | 500 |

All the examples above are compatible pairs.

---

125 + 75   19 + 31

134 + 23   43 + 7

72 + 16   280 + 20

405 + 27   78 + 22

455 + 45   131 + 17

82 + 18

Which of these problems contain compatible numbers?

What are the "tidy" sums?

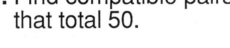

TRY THESE IN YOUR HEAD.

1. Find compatible pairs that total 50.

48	20	39
19	2	37	31
30	13	11

2. Find compatible pairs that total 200.

175	70	95
105	120	145	25
80	55	130

POWER BUILDER A

1. 27 + 23 = _____

2. 41 + 59 = _____

3. 74 + 26 = _____

4. 14 + 36 = _____

5. 237 + 63 = _____

6. 145 + 55 = _____

7. 42 + 58 = _____

8. 134 + 66 = _____

9. 120 + 380 = _____

10. 131 + 69 = _____

11. 21 + _____ = 50

12. 32 + _____ = 50

13. 37 + _____ = 100

14. 48 + _____ = 100

15. 61 + _____ = 100

16. 45 + _____ = 200

17. 134 + _____ = 200

18. 165 + _____ = 200

19. 162 + _____ = 300

20. 198 + _____ = 500

THINK IT THROUGH

Add these numbers:
the largest two-digit number,
the smallest three-digit odd number,
the largest one-digit number, and
the smallest two-digit odd number.
What do you get?

POWER BUILDER B

1. 48 + 52 = _____

2. 11 + 39 = _____

3. 65 + 35 = _____

4. 23 + 27 = _____

5. 68 + 32 = _____

6. 91 + 109 = _____

7. 134 + 166 = _____

8. 448 + 52 = _____

9. 119 + 81 = _____

10. 235 + 65 = _____

11. 47 + _____ = 50

12. 38 + _____ = 50

13. 45 + _____ = 100

14. 39 + _____ = 100

15. 73 + _____ = 100

16. 118 + _____ = 200

17. 144 + _____ = 200

18. 139 + _____ = 200

19. 125 + _____ = 300

20. 246 + _____ = 500

THINK IT THROUGH

Add these numbers:
the largest odd number less than 60,
the smallest odd number,
the largest one-digit even number, and
the smallest two-digit even number.
What do you get?

When you have a chain
of numbers to add in
your head, it's easy if
you do it

  ⌐one
    ⌐step
      ⌐at
        ⌐a
          ⌐time.

$$130 + 50 + 70 + 20 + 50$$
$$180 + 70$$
$$250 + 20$$
$$270 + 50$$
$$320$$

Here's another trick to make
a chain easy to handle:

Look for compatible pairs.

200

130 + 50 + **70** + 20 + 50

100

200 plus 100 is 300,
plus 20 is 320.

TRY THESE IN YOUR HEAD.

Look for compatible pairs.

1. 60 + 75 + 40   **6.** 80 + 50 + 20 + 75 + 25

2. 45 + 35 + 15   **7.** 75 + 60 + 25 + 15 + 40

3. 60 + 45 + 50 + 5   **8.** 15 + 20 + 25 + 35 + 30

4. 35 + 30 + 15 + 70   **9.** 40 + 75 + 50 + 60 + 25

5. 20 + 35 + 15 + 80 + 40   **10.** 85 + 65 + 35 + 15 + 75 + 25

POWER BUILDER A

1. 30 + 25 + 20 = _____

2. 40 + 80 + 60 = _____

3. 35 + 15 + 85 = _____

4. 20 + 45 + 80 = _____

5. 65 + 50 + 35 = _____

6. 45 + 55 + 85 + 15 = _____

7. 25 + 65 + 75 + 10 = _____

8. 45 + 65 + 55 + 15 = _____

9. 85 + 25 + 15 + 75 = _____

10. 65 + 25 + 35 + 70 = _____

11. 40 + 25 + 10 = _____

12. 70 + 65 + 30 = _____

13. 55 + 45 + 35 = _____

14. 75 + 65 + 25 = _____

15. 85 + 75 + 15 = _____

16. 45 + 35 + 65 + 25 = _____

17. 15 + 95 + 85 + 10 = _____

18. 35 + 65 + 75 + 75 = _____

19. 45 + 25 + 55 + 50 = _____

20. 75 + 65 + 35 + 15 = _____

THINK IT THROUGH

What is the sum of 96, 97, 98, 99, 100, 101, 102, 103, and 104? Look for a shortcut.

POWER BUILDER B

1. 20 + 35 + 15 = _____

2. 70 + 45 + 30 = _____

3. 85 + 15 + 65 = _____

4. 30 + 55 + 70 = _____

5. 15 + 75 + 85 = _____

6. 85 + 15 + 75 + 10 = _____

7. 35 + 65 + 55 + 45 = _____

8. 95 + 25 + 75 + 10 = _____

9. 85 + 45 + 15 + 35 = _____

10. 45 + 45 + 65 + 35 = _____

11. 45 + 25 + 55 = _____

12. 65 + 15 + 35 = _____

13. 45 + 55 + 75 = _____

14. 25 + 65 + 35 = _____

15. 75 + 75 + 45 = _____

16. 55 + 25 + 50 + 45 = _____

17. 15 + 35 + 55 + 20 = _____

18. 45 + 35 + 55 + 20 = _____

19. 45 + 55 + 45 + 15 = _____

20. 65 + 25 + 35 + 35 = _____

THINK IT THROUGH

Find the sum of all the whole numbers from 45 to 55 (including both 45 and 55). Be sure to look for a shortcut.

That looks too hard to do in my head!

$25 + 79$

Look for compatible numbers.
If they aren't there . . . make your own!

You can do it by breaking up one number . . .

$25 + 79$

$$25 + 75 \rightarrow \begin{array}{r} 100 \\ + \ 4 \\ \hline 104 \end{array}$$

Or you can round up, then adjust the total.

$25 + 79$

$$25 + 80 \rightarrow \begin{array}{r} 105 \\ - \ 1 \\ \hline 104 \end{array}$$

TRY THESE IN YOUR HEAD.

Make your own compatible pairs.

(50–3)

(25+3)

1. $75 + 28$
2. $25 + 29$
3. $47 + 150$
4. $25 + 79$
5. $175 + 22$
6. $226 + 75$
7. $148 + 50$
8. $350 + 72$
9. $328 + 25$
10. $235 + 17$

POWER BUILDER A

1. 25 + 28 = _____
2. 25 + 77 = _____
3. 75 + 26 = _____
4. 75 + 78 = _____
5. 25 + 27 = _____
6. 27 + 75 = _____
7. 175 + 29 = _____
8. 225 + 78 = _____
9. 175 + 58 = _____
10. 57 + 75 = _____

11. 25 + 49 = _____
12. 58 + 75 = _____
13. 149 + 50 = _____
14. 275 + 28 = _____
15. 29 + 125 = _____
16. 58 + 225 = _____
17. 98 + 25 = _____
18. 197 + 75 = _____
19. 75 + 19 = _____
20. 225 + 49 = _____

THINK IT THROUGH

Think of the smallest two-digit odd number. Double it. Add 18. Subtract 15. What is the result?

POWER BUILDER B

1. 75 + 28 = _____
2. 25 + 26 = _____
3. 75 + 77 = _____
4. 25 + 29 = _____
5. 28 + 25 = _____
6. 26 + 75 = _____
7. 78 + 25 = _____
8. 175 + 57 = _____
9. 59 + 175 = _____
10. 157 + 75 = _____

11. 25 + 48 = _____
12. 75 + 56 = _____
13. 375 + 28 = _____
14. 147 + 75 = _____
15. 125 + 28 = _____
16. 98 + 75 = _____
17. 199 + 75 = _____
18. 23 + 175 = _____
19. 49 + 325 = _____
20. 78 + 175 = _____

THINK IT THROUGH

Think of the largest two-digit even number. Subtract 38. Add 25. Subtract 45. Add 15. Subtract 55. What is the result?

68

Mental Math Techniques
• **START AT THE LEFT** $56 + 27 = ?$ $947 - 536 = ?$
• **MAKE BOTH END IN 5.** $25 + 119 = 25 + 115 + 4 = ?$
• **MAKE 10'S AND TRADE OFF.** $67 + 24 = 70 + 21 = ?$
• **MAKE 10'S AND BALANCE.** $72 - 39 = 73 - 40 = ?$
• **SEARCH FOR COMPATIBLES.** $20 + 75 + 80 = ?$ $100 - 17 = ?$
• **MAKE YOUR OWN COMPATIBLES.** $248 + 60 = 240 + 8 + 60 = ?$

Do the problems below in your head. Tell which techniques you find useful for each one.

1. $29 + 64$
2. $396 - 145$
3. $135 + 10 + 15$
4. $19 + 75$
5. $93 - 49$
6. $67 + 24$
7. $27 + 175$
8. $70 + 25 + 125 + 30$
9. $1000 - 450$
10. $297 + 50$

Talk about each problem below. What's an easy way to do it in your head? Tell how you would think it through.

1. $50 + 20 + 30 + 35$
2. $54 - 18$
3. $77 + 16$
4. $18 + 58$
5. $478 - 227$
6. $25 + 28$
7. $100 - 57$
8. $838 - 524$
9. $35 + 39$
10. $45 + 17$
11. $158 + 153$
12. $694 - 79$

1. 65 + 35 + 45 = _____

2. 45 + 49 = _____

3. 80 − 71 = _____

4. 49 + 15 = _____

5. 1000 − 25 = _____

6. 42 − 19 = _____

7. 57 − 21 = _____

8. 95 + 59 = _____

9. 100 − 19 = _____

10. 38 + 39 = _____

11. 48 + 47 = _____

12. 843 − 220 = _____

13. 65 + 27 = _____

14. 85 − 28 = _____

15. 100 − 45 = _____

16. 80 + 40 + 20 + 60 = _____

17. 477 − 236 = _____

18. 17 + 46 = _____

19. 55 − 27 = _____

20. 38 + 36 = _____

21. 200 − 144 = _____

22. 88 + 30 + 15 + 5 = _____

23. 81 − 25 = _____

24. 26 + 36 = _____

25. 1000 − 730 = _____

26. 145 + 29 = _____

27. 83 − 59 = _____

28. 54 − 38 = _____

29. 1000 − 750 = _____

30. 381 − 120 = _____

31. 75 + 79 = _____

32. 57 + 18 = _____

33. 500 − 198 = _____

34. 45 + 25 + 55 + 50 = _____

35. 7934 − 5132 = _____

36. 90 − 31 = _____

37. 175 + 18 + 15 + 10 = _____

38. 100 − 36 = _____

39. 48 + 37 = _____

40. 53 + 47 = _____

MENTAL MATH IN THE MIDDLE GRADES
Copyright © 1987 by Dale Seymour Publications

Complicated Mental Calculations

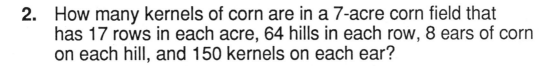

MENTALMATHLETES often start calculating in their heads at a very young age. For example, Zerah Colburn could compute very difficult calculations mentally even before he started school. He answered the following questions without pencil and paper when he was just 6 years old:

1. Multiply 12,225 and 1,223.

   His answer: 14,951,175

2. How many kernels of corn are in a 7-acre corn field that has 17 rows in each acre, 64 hills in each row, 8 ears of corn on each hill, and 150 kernels on each ear?

   His answer: 9,139,200 kernels

3. If a clock strikes 156 times in one day, how many times will it strike in 2000 years?

   His answer: 113,880,000 times

4. How many seconds are there in 2000 years?

   His answer: 63,072,000,000 seconds

How would YOU solve these problems?
Check to see if Zerah's answers were correct.
Use a calculator or check by "casting out nines."

Complicated Mental Calculations

Ask the students to discuss how problems 2, 3, and 4 could be solved before you have them check young Zerah Colburn's answers.

As the answers to problems 3 and 4 will overload most hand-held calculators, discuss how we could use pencil-and-paper methods combined with a calculator to check the answers.

Casting Out Nines
Before calculators were invented, it was tedious work to check the answers given by a good mental calculator. But there's a shortcut method, called "casting out nines," that we can use to check calculations with large numbers. Students generally enjoy learning to cast out nines, as follows:

To check that 12,225 $\times$ 1,223 = 14,951,175, "cast out nines" by adding the digits of each number until you get a single-digit remainder, as shown in the computation below:

12,225 . . . $1 + 2 + 2 + 2 + 5 = 12$ . . . $1 + 2 = 3$ . . . remainder = 3

1, 223 . . . $1 + 2 + 2 + 3 = 8$ . . . remainder = 8

14,951,175 . . . $1 + 4 + 9 + 5 + 1 + 1 + 7 + 5 = 33$ . . . $3 + 3 = 6$ . . . remainder = 6

Then multiply the remainders of each factor and cast out nines again:
$3 \times 8 = 24$ . . . $2 + 4 = 6$ . . . remainder = 6

Since this remainder (6) equals the remainder obtained for Colburn's answer (14,951,175), there is **likely** no error in the computation.

Have the students cast out nines to check Colburn's other answers.

Other Mentalmathletes
Another young Mentalmathlete was Jacques Inaudi, who lived 100 years ago. He could multiply two 5-digit numbers in his head at age seven—but he didn't learn to read and write until he was twenty!

Today's "mental math" record holder in the Guinness book is Mrs. Shakuntala Devi of India. She multiplied these two numbers in her head:
7,686,369,774,870 $\times$ 2,465,099,745,779
She did it in 28 seconds, and she got the correct answer!

To find out about other great "mentalmathletes," look for the book *The Great Mental Calculators* by Steven Smith (Columbia University Press, 1983).

Does counting by 25 seem hard to you?

Try thinking of quarters.

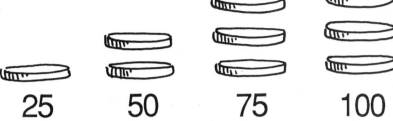

| 25 | 50 | 75 | 100 |

Think of counting out $5 in quarters.

25	50	75	100
125	150	175	200
225	250	275	300
325	350	375	400
425	450	475	500

What pattern do you see?

Use that pattern to help you
add these in your head.

$125 + 25 + 25 = ?$

$75 + 25 + 50 = ?$

TRY THESE IN YOUR HEAD.

Think quarters.

1. 50 + 25
2. 150 + 25
3. 250 + 25
4. 225 + 25 + 25
5. 100 + 25 + 25

6. 350 + 25
7. 75 + 50
8. 225 + 50
9. 250 + 75 + 25
10. 125 + 25 + 50 + 25

MENTAL MATH IN THE MIDDLE GRADES
Copyright © 1987 by Dale Seymour Publications

POWER BUILDER A

1. 75 + 25 = _____

2. 50 + 25 = _____

3. 225 + 25 = _____

4. 100 + 25 + 25 = _____

5. 300 + 50 = _____

6. 175 + 25 + 25 = _____

7. 75 + 50 = _____

8. 75 + 25 + 50 = _____

9. 325 + 50 = _____

10. 225 + 25 + 50 = _____

11. 175 + 25 + 25 = _____

12. 650 + 25 + 50 = _____

13. 400 + 75 + 50 = _____

14. 50 + 75 + 25 = _____

15. 250 + 75 + 50 = _____

16. 350 + 75 + 50 = _____

17. 425 + 50 + 75 = _____

18. 200 + 75 + 50 = _____

19. 325 + 50 + 75 = _____

20. 250 + 75 + 75 = _____

THINK IT THROUGH

Suppose you had five quarters. Then someone gave you twice as many more. How much money do you have now?

POWER BUILDER B

1. 150 + 25 = _____

2. 75 + 25 = _____

3. 325 + 25 = _____

4. 200 + 50 + 25 = _____

5. 400 + 50 = _____

6. 275 + 25 + 25 = _____

7. 175 + 50 = _____

8. 75 + 25 + 50 = _____

9. 425 + 50 = _____

10. 325 + 25 + 50 = _____

11. 275 + 50 = _____

12. 550 + 25 + 50 = _____

13. 200 + 75 + 50 = _____

14. 150 + 75 + 25 = _____

15. 250 + 75 + 50 = _____

16. 550 + 75 + 50 = _____

17. 825 + 50 + 75 = _____

18. 300 + 50 + 75 = _____

19. 625 + 50 + 75 = _____

20. 350 + 75 + 75 = _____

THINK IT THROUGH

Suppose you had ten quarters. Then someone gave you half as much as you already had. But then you lost one quarter. How much money do you have now?

Did you ever wonder
why so many prices
end in 98 and 99?

Studies show that more
people will buy something
priced at $9.99 than at $10.
That's why we see prices like these.

In mental math, you can clean up numbers
ending in 8 or 9 to make them easy to add.

Round up . . .   add . . .   then adjust.

$$300 + 450 \rightarrow 750$$
$$\underline{- 1}$$
$$749$$

$8 + $4 → $13
minus 2 cents = $12.98

TRY THESE IN YOUR HEAD.
Clean up the 8's and 9's.

1. 65 + 29	**3.** 254 + 499	**7.** $2.75 + $1.99
2. 88 + 69	**4.** 478 + 899	**8.** $11.50 + $3.99
	5. 265 + 98	**9.** $59.80 + $8.99
	6. 4314 + 898	**10.** $19.98 + $25.50

POWER BUILDER A

1. 35 + 29 = _____

2. 54 + 49 = _____

3. 26 + 98 = _____

4. 45 + 39 = _____

5. 56 + 29 = _____

6. 125 + 99 = _____

7. 423 + 498 = _____

8. 807 + 99 = _____

9. 244 + 699 = _____

10. 1524 + 299 = _____

11. $3.22 + $1.99 = _____

12. $0.75 + $0.98 = _____

13. $2.85 + $1.98 = _____

14. $15.35 + $0.98 = _____

15. $7.45 + $9.98 = _____

16. $4.25 + $1.99 = _____

17. $0.98 + $0.65 = _____

18. $2.35 + $1.99 = _____

19. $13.45 + $10.98 = _____

20. $5.98 + $9.99 = _____

THINK IT THROUGH

The price of a daily paper at the newsstand is $0.35 per copy. The regular subscription rate is $0.24 per copy. How much can you save per week by subscribing rather than buying a paper daily?

POWER BUILDER B

1. 25 + 49 = _____

2. 63 + 28 = _____

3. 45 + 98 = _____

4. 154 + 99 = _____

5. 199 + 267 = _____

6. 456 + 399 = _____

7. 2145 + 699 = _____

8. 399 + 198 = _____

9. 4256 + 498 = _____

10. 298 + 275 = _____

11. $0.26 + $0.99 = _____

12. $2.45 + $1.99 = _____

13. $0.87 + $0.98 = _____

14. $1.45 + $0.98 = _____

15. $4.52 + $4.99 = _____

16. $15.99 + $2.65 = _____

17. $7.98 + $9.75 = _____

18. $5.35 + $19.99 = _____

19. $45.86 + $29.99 = _____

20. $7.98 + $18.75 = _____

THINK IT THROUGH

The price of a monthly magazine at the newsstand is $1.75. The subscription rate is $1.00 per issue. How much can you save in a year by subscribing rather than buying the magazine monthly?

To **add** 8's and 9's in your head, you clean them up by rounding to "make tens," then adjust the answer.

$$\$ .99 + \$1.99$$

$1 + $2 → $3
minus 2 cents
or $2.98

Here's good news: The same idea works for subtraction!

$$75 - 29$$

$$
\begin{array}{r}
75 - 30 \rightarrow 45 \\
+ 1 \\
\hline
46
\end{array}
$$

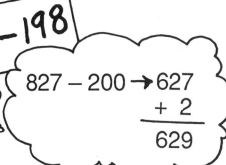

$$827 - 198$$

$$
\begin{array}{r}
827 - 200 \rightarrow 627 \\
+ 2 \\
\hline
629
\end{array}
$$

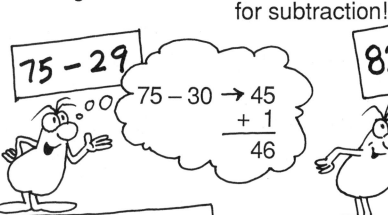

$$\$20 - \$15.98$$

$20 - $16 → $4
plus 2 cents = $4.02

TRY THESE IN YOUR HEAD.

Clean up the 8's and 9's.

1. 83 – 39   **3.** 427 – 198   **7.** $8.36 – $5.99

2. 95 – 59   **4.** 872 – 399   **8.** $20 – $13.98

                5. 265 – 98   **9.** $40 – $29.99

                6. 5236 – 999   **10.** $100 – $59.98

POWER BUILDER A

1. 82 − 29 = _____

2. 45 − 19 = _____

3. 265 − 98 = _____

4. 74 − 49 = _____

5. 81 − 28 = _____

6. 436 − 189 = _____

7. 724 − 199 = _____

8. 615 − 98 = _____

9. 246 − 198 = _____

10. 1754 − 999 = _____

11. $5.00 − $1.99 = _____

12. $5.00 − $0.98 = _____

13. $5.00 − $3.99 = _____

14. $10.00 − $3.98 = _____

15. $20.00 − $9.98 = _____

16. $20.00 − $14.99 = _____

17. $5.00 − $2.98 = _____

18. $10.00 − $4.99 = _____

19. $50.00 − $29.99 = _____

20. $20.00 − $4.98 = _____

THINK IT THROUGH

If you buy a pair of jeans for $11.99 and a belt for $5.99, how much change will you get back from $20.00? (Don't figure any tax.)

POWER BUILDER B

1. 64 − 29 = _____

2. 83 − 49 = _____

3. 75 − 48 = _____

4. 246 − 199 = _____

5. 435 − 299 = _____

6. 1527 − 999 = _____

7. 752 − 198 = _____

8. 4526 − 998 = _____

9. 1800 − 499 = _____

10. 1750 − 198 = _____

11. $0.75 − $0.59 = _____

12. $0.50 − $0.28 = _____

13. $2.00 − $0.98 = _____

14. $10.00 − $4.98 = _____

15. $20.00 − $15.99 = _____

16. $100.00 − $49.99 = _____

17. $50.00 − $19.98 = _____

18. $20.00 − $12.98 = _____

19. $20.00 − $8.99 = _____

20. $50.00 − $18.99 = _____

THINK IT THROUGH

If you buy one T-shirt for $8.98 and two records at $4.99 each, how much change will you get back from $20.00? (Don't figure any tax.)

Here's a simple way to multiply any number by 10, or 100, or 1000, in your head.

Look for a pattern in the zeros.

$5 \times \mathbf{10} = 5$ **tens** $= 5\mathbf{0}$
$5 \times \mathbf{100} = 5$ **hundreds** $= 5\mathbf{00}$
$5 \times \mathbf{1000} = 5$ **thousands** $= 5\mathbf{000}$

To multiply any number . . .

by 10   → tack on ONE trailing zero.
by 100   → tack on TWO trailing zeros.
by 1000 → tack on THREE trailing zeros.

$$9 \times 1000$$

Here's how a mental-math pro thinks . . .

9 **thousands** . . . so tack on three zeros after the 9.
9000

TRY THESE IN YOUR HEAD.
Tack on trailing zeros.

1. 3×10 **3.** 8×1000 **7.** 100×8

2. 7×100 **4.** 10×13 **8.** 7×1000

                            5. 23×100 **9.** 1000×14

                            6. 1000×11 **10.** 10×162

POWER BUILDER A

1. $2 \times 10 =$ _____
2. $5 \times 10 =$ _____
3. $10 \times 7 =$ _____
4. $4 \times 100 =$ _____
5. $3 \times 100 =$ _____
6. $1000 \times 5 =$ _____
7. $7 \times 1000 =$ _____
8. $2 \times 1000 =$ _____
9. $8 \times 100 =$ _____
10. $10 \times 9 =$ _____

11. $11 \times 10 =$ _____
12. $10 \times 27 =$ _____
13. $125 \times 10 =$ _____
14. $23 \times 100 =$ _____
15. $69 \times 100 =$ _____
16. $125 \times 100 =$ _____
17. $13 \times 1000 =$ _____
18. $1000 \times 18 =$ _____
19. $275 \times 1000 =$ _____
20. $1000 \times 51 =$ _____

THINK IT THROUGH

If I pay 26 cents for a paper and sell it for 35 cents, how much money will I make selling 100 papers?

POWER BUILDER B

1. $4 \times 10 =$ _____
2. $6 \times 10 =$ _____
3. $10 \times 3 =$ _____
4. $2 \times 100 =$ _____
5. $6 \times 100 =$ _____
6. $1000 \times 3 =$ _____
7. $6 \times 1000 =$ _____
8. $4 \times 1000 =$ _____
9. $100 \times 7 =$ _____
10. $15 \times 100 =$ _____

11. $13 \times 10 =$ _____
12. $19 \times 10 =$ _____
13. $10 \times 25 =$ _____
14. $27 \times 100 =$ _____
15. $100 \times 73 =$ _____
16. $375 \times 100 =$ _____
17. $19 \times 1000 =$ _____
18. $375 \times 1000 =$ _____
19. $1000 \times 12 =$ _____
20. $1000 \times 68 =$ _____

THINK IT THROUGH

John bought a baseball card for 30 cents and sold it for 45 cents. He then bought it back for 40 cents and sold it again for 50 cents. How much money did he make?

Here's a trick for multiplying in your head.
Look at the zeros. What's the pattern?

$5 \times 3\mathbf{0} = 5 \times 3$ **tens** $= 15 \times 1\mathbf{0} = 15\mathbf{0}$
$7 \times 4\mathbf{00} = 7 \times 4$ **hundreds** $= 28 \times 1\mathbf{00} = 28\mathbf{00}$
$6 \times 3\mathbf{000} = 6 \times 3$ **thousands** $= 18 \times 1\mathbf{000} = 18,\mathbf{000}$

When one number has trailing zeros . . .

  1. Cut off the trailing zeros.

2. Multiply the remaining numbers.

3. Tack the trailing zeros onto your answer.

Here's how a
mental-math
pro thinks . . .

9×5000

$9 \times 5\boxed{000}$

$45,\boxed{000}$

TRY THESE IN YOUR HEAD.

Tack on the right number of zeros.

1. 5×30	**3.** 8×800	**7.** 8×70
2. 60×4	**4.** 9×40	**8.** 7×700
	5. 2×4000	**9.** 200×13
	6. 12×200	**10.** 3000×8

POWER BUILDER A

1. $4 \times 80 =$ _____
2. $70 \times 7 =$ _____
3. $9 \times 90 =$ _____
4. $80 \times 3 =$ _____
5. $12 \times 30 =$ _____
6. $4 \times 500 =$ _____
7. $900 \times 5 =$ _____
8. $800 \times 6 =$ _____
9. $8 \times 300 =$ _____
10. $12 \times 200 =$ _____

11. $3000 \times 9 =$ _____
12. $4 \times 2000 =$ _____
13. $8 \times 3000 =$ _____
14. $7 \times 7000 =$ _____
15. $12 \times 4000 =$ _____
16. $7 \times 6000 =$ _____
17. $8 \times 90 =$ _____
18. $500 \times 5 =$ _____
19. $8 \times 7000 =$ _____
20. $4 \times 400 =$ _____

THINK IT THROUGH

Which are worth more:
40 nickels or 25 dimes?

POWER BUILDER B

1. $8 \times 80 =$ _____
2. $10 \times 7 =$ _____
3. $9 \times 30 =$ _____
4. $80 \times 4 =$ _____
5. $12 \times 20 =$ _____
6. $5 \times 500 =$ _____
7. $900 \times 2 =$ _____
8. $800 \times 2 =$ _____
9. $3 \times 300 =$ _____
10. $11 \times 700 =$ _____

11. $4000 \times 7 =$ _____
12. $5 \times 8000 =$ _____
13. $8 \times 2000 =$ _____
14. $7 \times 3000 =$ _____
15. $11 \times 4000 =$ _____
16. $6 \times 600 =$ _____
17. $9 \times 60 =$ _____
18. $4000 \times 5 =$ _____
19. $7 \times 800 =$ _____
20. $8 \times 4000 =$ _____

THINK IT THROUGH

Which are worth the most:
35 nickels, 20 dimes, or 7 quarters?

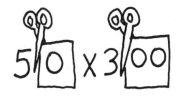

You can multiply this quickly
in your head.
Just follow these steps:

$5 \times 3 = 15$

- Cut off the trailing zeros.

- Multiply the remaining numbers.

- Collect ALL the zeros and tack
them onto your answer.

Here's how a
mental-math
pro thinks . . .

$$400 \times 30$$
$$4 \times 3 = 12$$
$$12{,}000$$

TRY THESE IN YOUR HEAD.

Tack on ALL the trailing zeros.

1. 20×50　　**3.** 300×300　　**7.** 50×50

2. 400×90　　**4.** 80×900　　**8.** 70×3000

　　　　　　　　　　5. 60×200　　**9.** 60×70

　　　　　　　　　　6. 7000×500　**10.** 120×40

POWER BUILDER A

1. $10 \times 10 =$ _____

2. $20 \times 20 =$ _____

3. $40 \times 50 =$ _____

4. $90 \times 90 =$ _____

5. $60 \times 70 =$ _____

6. $500 \times 20 =$ _____

7. $30 \times 400 =$ _____

8. $900 \times 10 =$ _____

9. $50 \times 500 =$ _____

10. $700 \times 80 =$ _____

11. $500 \times 500 =$ _____

12. $300 \times 700 =$ _____

13. $800 \times 100 =$ _____

14. $100 \times 100 =$ _____

15. $900 \times 900 =$ _____

16. $10 \times 2000 =$ _____

17. $20 \times 8000 =$ _____

18. $5000 \times 60 =$ _____

19. $80 \times 4000 =$ _____

20. $800 \times 1000 =$ _____

THINK IT THROUGH

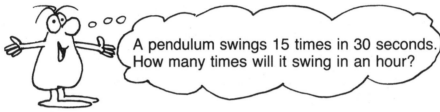

A pendulum swings 15 times in 30 seconds. How many times will it swing in an hour?

POWER BUILDER B

1. $40 \times 40 =$ _____

2. $30 \times 20 =$ _____

3. $40 \times 70 =$ _____

4. $80 \times 80 =$ _____

5. $90 \times 70 =$ _____

6. $200 \times 50 =$ _____

7. $40 \times 300 =$ _____

8. $800 \times 10 =$ _____

9. $30 \times 300 =$ _____

10. $800 \times 70 =$ _____

11. $600 \times 600 =$ _____

12. $700 \times 300 =$ _____

13. $500 \times 100 =$ _____

14. $200 \times 100 =$ _____

15. $800 \times 800 =$ _____

16. $20 \times 2000 =$ _____

17. $80 \times 2000 =$ _____

18. $6000 \times 50 =$ _____

19. $40 \times 8000 =$ _____

20. $700 \times 1000 =$ _____

THINK IT THROUGH

My heart beats 20 times in 15 seconds. How many times will it beat in an hour?

84

$$52 \times 7$$

Can you multiply this in your head?

It's easy if you break up one factor into smaller parts. Like this . . .

BREAK UP 52 . . . $52 \rightarrow 50 + 2$

MULTIPLY THE PARTS, STARTING AT THE LEFT . . . $\times \quad 7$

ADD . . . $350 + 14 = 364$

SO . . . $7 \times 52 = 364$

MENTAL MATH TIP $\Longrightarrow$

Think of it as multiplying from the left.

$$\begin{array}{r} 5\ 2 \\ \times \quad 7 \\ \hline \end{array}$$

TRY THESE IN YOUR HEAD.

Multiply from the left.

1. 15×7 **3.** 36×8 **7.** 3×28

2. 23×5 **4.** 3×54 **8.** 7×27

                      5. 16×8 **9.** 85×50

                      6. 31×4 **10.** 20×28

POWER BUILDER A

1. 31 × 7 = _____

2. 41 × 3 = _____

3. 4 × 22 = _____

4. 3 × 83 = _____

5. 5 × 51 = _____

6. 6 × 83 = _____

7. 8 × 94 = _____

8. 5 × 58 = _____

9. 2 × 78 = _____

10. 56 × 2 = _____

11. 8 × 58 = _____

12. 6 × 66 = _____

13. 4 × 48 = _____

14. 2 × 96 = _____

15. 7 × 77 = _____

16. 2 × 59 = _____

17. 7 × 51 = _____

18. 30 × 41 = _____

19. 25 × 30 = _____

20. 55 × 40 = _____

THINK IT THROUGH

Which two different whole numbers that add to 20 will give the largest product?

POWER BUILDER B

1. 21 × 7 = _____

2. 41 × 2 = _____

3. 3 × 22 = _____

4. 2 × 84 = _____

5. 4 × 51 = _____

6. 6 × 74 = _____

7. 9 × 83 = _____

8. 65 × 5 = _____

9. 87 × 2 = _____

10. 55 × 3 = _____

11. 4 × 45 = _____

12. 5 × 55 = _____

13. 5 × 58 = _____

14. 2 × 76 = _____

15. 6 × 96 = _____

16. 2 × 48 = _____

17. 6 × 57 = _____

18. 30 × 52 = _____

19. 20 × 25 = _____

20. 45 × 50 = _____

THINK IT THROUGH

Which two odd numbers that add to 20 will give the smallest product?

MULTIPLY IN
YOUR HEAD

$$\begin{array}{r} 625 \\ \times\ 4 \\ \hline \end{array}$$

625? But how can I work with such a large number in my head?

EASY.
Break it up into smaller parts.

Like this . . .

BREAK UP 625 . . .

MULTIPLY THE PARTS
FROM THE LEFT . . .

ADD . . .

$$\begin{array}{r} 600 + 25 \\ \times\ \qquad 4 \\ \hline 2400 + 100 = 2500 \end{array}$$

Now try this one.
How will you break up 423?

$$\begin{array}{r} 423 \\ \times\ 3 \\ \hline \end{array}$$

TRY THESE IN YOUR HEAD.

Multiply from the left.

1. 8×625 **3.** 112×8 **7.** 4×521

2. 4×256 **4.** 5×125 **8.** 3×252

5. 525×2 **9.** 507×8

6. 611×4 **10.** 7×911

POWER BUILDER A

1. $2 \times 434 = $ _____

2. $121 \times 5 = $ _____

3. $4 \times 124 = $ _____

4. $135 \times 2 = $ _____

5. $325 \times 3 = $ _____

6. $7 \times 303 = $ _____

7. $9 \times 209 = $ _____

8. $801 \times 6 = $ _____

9. $505 \times 5 = $ _____

10. $9 \times 111 = $ _____

11. $2 \times 435 = $ _____

12. $165 \times 5 = $ _____

13. $188 \times 5 = $ _____

14. $525 \times 8 = $ _____

15. $4 \times 256 = $ _____

16. $123 \times 3 = $ _____

17. $525 \times 4 = $ _____

18. $4 \times 625 = $ _____

19. $5 \times 808 = $ _____

20. $505 \times 6 = $ _____

THINK IT THROUGH

Pick three two-digit numbers. Multiply each number by 101. What pattern do you notice?

POWER BUILDER B

1. $2 \times 344 = $ _____

2. $122 \times 5 = $ _____

3. $4 \times 123 = $ _____

4. $148 \times 2 = $ _____

5. $425 \times 3 = $ _____

6. $404 \times 7 = $ _____

7. $309 \times 4 = $ _____

8. $6 \times 801 = $ _____

9. $5 \times 705 = $ _____

10. $519 \times 2 = $ _____

11. $2 \times 345 = $ _____

12. $145 \times 5 = $ _____

13. $166 \times 5 = $ _____

14. $425 \times 8 = $ _____

15. $4 \times 255 = $ _____

16. $3 \times 213 = $ _____

17. $505 \times 4 = $ _____

18. $3 \times 423 = $ _____

19. $235 \times 2 = $ _____

20. $9 \times 311 = $ _____

THINK IT THROUGH

Study these problems: $114 \times 1001 = 114,114$
$236 \times 1001 = 236,236$
Use the pattern to multiply these:
472×1001 203×1001 47×1001

There's an easy
way to multiply
this in your head.

6×99

THINK . . .   99 is ONE less than 100.

SO . . . 6×99 is SIX less than 600.

$$6 \times 99 = 600 - 6 = 594$$

This is a good strategy
to use with prices.

At $8.99 each, what would
6 robots cost?

Figure it out in your head!

TRY THESE IN YOUR HEAD.
Clean up the 9's, then adjust.

1. 8×99	**3.** 19×6	**7.** 15 at $1.99
2. 7×199	**4.** 29×5	**8.** 4 at $0.99
	5. 6 at $4.99	**9.** 3 at $2.49
	6. 3 at $1.49	**10.** 8 at $3.99

POWER BUILDER A

1. $4 \times 79 =$ _____

2. $8 \times 79 =$ _____

3. $3 \times 79 =$ _____

4. $6 \times 79 =$ _____

5. $2 \times 79 =$ _____

6. $8 \times 199 =$ _____

7. $6 \times 399 =$ _____

8. $5 \times 599 =$ _____

9. $3 \times 799 =$ _____

10. $2 \times 1999 =$ _____

11. $5 \times \$7.99 =$ _____

12. $2 \times \$39.99 =$ _____

13. $4 \times \$11.99 =$ _____

14. $3 \times \$19.99 =$ _____

15. $7 \times \$7.99 =$ _____

16. $3 \times \$2.99 =$ _____

17. $5 \times \$19.99 =$ _____

18. $4 \times \$1.99 =$ _____

19. $15 \times \$3.99 =$ _____

20. $5 \times \$49.99 =$ _____

THINK IT THROUGH

What is the mystery number? Clue: If you subtract the mystery number from 1000, you get a difference that is equal to 3 times 199.

POWER BUILDER B

1. $8 \times 39 =$ _____

2. $6 \times 59 =$ _____

3. $4 \times 89 =$ _____

4. $5 \times 79 =$ _____

5. $7 \times 29 =$ _____

6. $8 \times 29 =$ _____

7. $6 \times 499 =$ _____

8. $5 \times 699 =$ _____

9. $3 \times 899 =$ _____

10. $3 \times 2999 =$ _____

11. $6 \times \$3.99 =$ _____

12. $3 \times \$19.99 =$ _____

13. $2 \times \$59.99 =$ _____

14. $7 \times \$1.99 =$ _____

15. $4 \times \$6.99 =$ _____

16. $6 \times \$1.99 =$ _____

17. $3 \times \$9.99 =$ _____

18. $5 \times \$29.99 =$ _____

19. $2 \times \$17.99 =$ _____

20. $25 \times \$1.99 =$ _____

THINK IT THROUGH

What is the mystery number? Clue: The mystery number is twice as much as 2 times 49.

Mental Math Techniques
• **THINK QUARTERS.**
550 + 125 + 50 = ?
• **CLEAN UP 8'S AND 9'S.**
TO ADD ... 198 + 499 = ?
TO SUBTRACT ... 672 − 98 = ?
TO MULTIPLY ... 7 × $3.99 = ?
• **TACK ON TRAILING ZEROS.**
9 × 100 = ?   60 × 400 = ?
• **MULTIPLY FROM THE LEFT.**
8 × 23 = ?   253 × 4 = ?

Do the problems below in your head. Tell which techniques you find useful for each one.

1. 4 × 399
2. 508 × 4
3. $3.47 + $1.99
4. 425 + 75 + 75
5. 7 × 400
6. 733 − 299
7. 247 + 399
8. 5 × $19.99
9. 200 × 900
10. 213 × 3

Talk about each problem below. What's an easy way to do it in your head? Tell how you would think it through.

1. 574 − 98
2. 275 + 50 + 25
3. 5 × 60
4. 8 × 425
5. $45.00 − $14.99
6. 5 × 130

7. 98 + 140
8. 20 × $1.99
9. 150 + 125
10. 30 × 30
11. 8 × 69
12. 50 × 800

MENTAL MATH PROGRESS TEST

1. 50 × 50 = _____

2. 3 × 424 = _____

3. 199 + 45 = _____

4. 79 + 25 = _____

5. 75 − 39 = _____

6. 125 + 50 = _____

7. 6 × 40 = _____

8. $54.99 + $3.25 = _____

9. 3000 × 5 = _____

10. 40 × 70 = _____

11. 4 × 26 = _____

12. 8 × 600 = _____

13. 50 + 25 + 75 = _____

14. 73 × 5 = _____

15. 98 + 67 = _____

16. 6 × 806 = _____

17. 95 − 29 = _____

18. 215 + 98 = _____

19. 8 × 625 = _____

20. 5275 − 1999 = _____

21. 225 + 50 + 50 = _____

22. 200 × 11 = _____

23. 5 × $2.99 = _____

24. $10.00 − $5.98 = _____

25. 255 × 2 = _____

26. 325 + 50 + 25 = _____

27. 900 × 6 = _____

28. $4.98 + $8.99 = _____

29. 100 × 6 = _____

30. 50 × 7 = _____

31. 12 × 300 = _____

32. 299 + 81 = _____

33. 3 × $2.49 = _____

34. $45.99 + $9.99 = _____

35. 149 + 45 = _____

36. 9 × 1000 = _____

37. 625 + 50 + 125 = _____

38. $20.00 − $13.98 = _____

39. 4019 + 298 = _____

40. 8 × 599 = _____

An Interesting Number Pattern

MENTALMATHLETE Arthur Benjamin enjoyed thinking about number patterns. One day while traveling downtown on a bus, he started thinking about pairs of numbers that add to 20. He noticed an interesting pattern when he multiplied those pairs:

$$9 \times 11 = 10 \times 10 - 1$$

$$8 \times 12 = 10 \times 10 - 4$$

$$7 \times 13 = 10 \times 10 - 9$$

1. Can you complete his pattern?

2. Find a similar pattern for pairs of numbers that add to 40. Explain how such a pattern could be used to calculate mentally problems like these:

$$19 \times 21 \qquad 18 \times 22 \qquad 17 \times 23$$

$$29 \times 31 \qquad 28 \times 32 \qquad 27 \times 33$$

An Interesting Number Pattern

1. The pattern that Arthur Benjamin noticed continues as follows:
$$6 \times 14 = 10 \times 10 - 16$$
$$5 \times 15 = 10 \times 10 - 25$$
$$4 \times 16 = 10 \times 10 - 36$$
$$3 \times 17 = 10 \times 10 - 49$$
$$2 \times 18 = 10 \times 10 - 64$$
$$1 \times 19 = 10 \times 10 - 81$$

2. A similar pattern for sums to 40 is as follows:
$$19 \times 21 = 20 \times 20 - 1$$
$$18 \times 22 = 20 \times 20 - 4$$
$$17 \times 23 = 20 \times 20 - 9$$
and so forth.

This pattern exists for any chosen sum. You can use such a pattern to simplify mental calculations like those shown at the bottom of this "Mentalmathletes" page. That is:

Think of 19×21 as $20 \times 20 - 1$, or 399.
Think of 18×22 as $20 \times 20 - 4$, or 396.
Think of 17×23 as $20 \times 20 - 9$, or 391.

Think of 29×31 as $30 \times 30 - 1$, or 899.
Think of 28×32 as $30 \times 30 - 4$, or 896.
Think of 27×33 as $30 \times 30 - 9$, or 891.

How much for **two** of those?

The price has **doubled** since last year!

You have **twice** as many as I do.

Doubling numbers is something we do every day. Here's an easy way to do it in your head:

Double a number by doubling each of its parts. Then add.

DOUBLE 48

double 40 . . .	80
double 8 . . .	16
	96

DOUBLE 126

double 100 . . .	200
double 20 . . .	40
double 6 . . .	12
	252

TRY THESE IN YOUR HEAD.

Double each number by parts.

1. Double 34   **3.** Double 912   **7.** Double 64

2. Double 81   **4.** Double 47   **8.** Double 75

5. Double 29   **9.** Double 54

6. Double 430   **10.** Double 720

POWER BUILDER A

1. Double 23 = _____

2. Double 62 = _____

3. Double 210 = _____

4. Double 207 = _____

5. Double 45 = _____

6. Double 508 = _____

7. Double 57 = _____

8. Double 98 = _____

9. Double 250 = _____

10. Double 900 = _____

11. Double 42 = _____

12. Double 91 = _____

13. Double 325 = _____

14. Double 36 = _____

15. Double 55 = _____

16. Double 86 = _____

17. Double 64 = _____

18. Double 128 = _____

19. Double 256 = _____

20. Double 512 = _____

THINK IT THROUGH

Think of a number. Double it. Add 6. Divide by 2. Subtract the number you thought of first. Now do the same thing with a new starting number. Can you explain why your answer is always 3?

POWER BUILDER B

1. Double 43 = _____

2. Double 74 = _____

3. Double 113 = _____

4. Double 16 = _____

5. Double 85 = _____

6. Double 700 = _____

7. Double 87 = _____

8. Double 97 = _____

9. Double 65 = _____

10. Double 840 = _____

11. Double 34 = _____

12. Double 83 = _____

13. Double 424 = _____

14. Double 409 = _____

15. Double 75 = _____

16. Double 27 = _____

17. Double 54 = _____

18. Double 108 = _____

19. Double 216 = _____

20. Double 432 = _____

THINK IT THROUGH

Think of a number. Multiply it by 4. Subtract 8. Divide by 4. Add 2. Now do the same thing with a new starting number. Can you explain your answer?

$$4 \times 15$$

Here's a trick to make mental multiplication easier.

If one number is even, you can cut it in half and double the other number.

This sometimes gives you an easier problem.

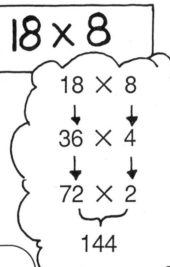

HALF OF 4 . . . DOUBLE 15

$$2 \times 30$$
THAT'S EASY!

60

You can even keep on halving and doubling, if it helps . . .

$$18 \times 8$$

18 × 8

↓   ↓

36 × 4

↓   ↓

72 × 2

144

TRY THESE IN YOUR HEAD.

Halve one, double the other.

1. 4 × 17
2. 6 × 45

3. 5 × 68
4. 35 × 4
5. 25 × 16
6. 125 × 12

7. 8 × 13
8. 12 × 150
9. 8 × 45
10. 55 × 6

POWER BUILDER A

1. $4 \times 13 =$ _____

2. $6 \times 15 =$ _____

3. $8 \times 35 =$ _____

4. $23 \times 4 =$ _____

5. $35 \times 6 =$ _____

6. $4 \times 55 =$ _____

7. $6 \times 65 =$ _____

8. $8 \times 15 =$ _____

9. $37 \times 4 =$ _____

10. $25 \times 6 =$ _____

11. $14 \times 15 =$ _____

12. $15 \times 32 =$ _____

13. $14 \times 25 =$ _____

14. $18 \times 25 =$ _____

15. $250 \times 16 =$ _____

16. $150 \times 6 =$ _____

17. $150 \times 14 =$ _____

18. $125 \times 8 =$ _____

19. $14 \times 35 =$ _____

20. $12 \times 150 =$ _____

THINK IT THROUGH

Use mental math to decide which of the following equals 64×32:

64×16 128×16
32×128 128×64

POWER BUILDER B

1. $4 \times 14 =$ _____

2. $6 \times 25 =$ _____

3. $8 \times 45 =$ _____

4. $24 \times 4 =$ _____

5. $45 \times 6 =$ _____

6. $4 \times 65 =$ _____

7. $6 \times 55 =$ _____

8. $8 \times 55 =$ _____

9. $47 \times 4 =$ _____

10. $75 \times 6 =$ _____

11. $18 \times 15 =$ _____

12. $16 \times 25 =$ _____

13. $15 \times 64 =$ _____

14. $24 \times 15 =$ _____

15. $225 \times 8 =$ _____

16. $150 \times 8 =$ _____

17. $16 \times 12 =$ _____

18. $125 \times 6 =$ _____

19. $18 \times 35 =$ _____

20. $15 \times 120 =$ _____

THINK IT THROUGH

Use mental math to decide which of the following equals 48×144:

24×96 24×72
96×288 96×72

98

These are all different ways to think
about the same division problem.

$$600 \div 10 \qquad 10\overline{)600} \qquad 600/10$$

600 DIVIDED BY 10

10 DIVIDES 600

Sometimes mental division
is easier if you multiply.
Think of it this way . . .

10 times WHAT NUMBER equals 600?

10 times [60] = 600

So . . . $600 \div 10 = 60$

(When you multiply, think
about trailing zeros.)

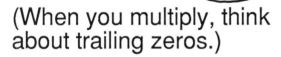
TRY THESE IN YOUR HEAD.

Divide by multiplying.

1. $400 \div 8$	**3.** $5\overline{)100}$	**7.** $300/3$
2. $60/10$	**4.** $40\overline{)200}$	**8.** $70\overline{)3500}$
	5. $800 \div 40$	**9.** $270 \div 27$
	6. $2400 \div 30$	**10.** $6000/20$

POWER BUILDER A

1. $50 \div 5 =$ _____

2. $60 \div 6 =$ _____

3. $10\overline{)80} =$ _____

4. $30 \div 10 =$ _____

5. $140 \div 20 =$ _____

6. $9\overline{)180} =$ _____

7. $160 \div 80 =$ _____

8. $110 \div 11 =$ _____

9. $80\overline{)240} =$ _____

10. $360 \div 9 =$ _____

11. $400/8 =$ _____

12. $60\overline{)480} =$ _____

13. $420 \div 6 =$ _____

14. $500/5 =$ _____

15. $70\overline{)630} =$ _____

16. $540 \div 6 =$ _____

17. $1200/20 =$ _____

18. $3\overline{)2700} =$ _____

19. $4900 \div 7 =$ _____

20. $6400/80 =$ _____

**THINK IT
THROUGH**

How many 25-cent stamps can
you buy with $10?

POWER BUILDER B

1. $40 \div 8 =$ _____

2. $70 \div 7 =$ _____

3. $10\overline{)90} =$ _____

4. $50 \div 10 =$ _____

5. $1200 \div 20 =$ _____

6. $7\overline{)140} =$ _____

7. $1200 \div 600 =$ _____

8. $120 \div 20 =$ _____

9. $90\overline{)270} =$ _____

10. $320 \div 8 =$ _____

11. $300/5 =$ _____

12. $70\overline{)420} =$ _____

13. $480 \div 8 =$ _____

14. $600/6 =$ _____

15. $90\overline{)5400} =$ _____

16. $630 \div 9 =$ _____

17. $1500/30 =$ _____

18. $2\overline{)1800} =$ _____

19. $5400 \div 6 =$ _____

20. $8100/9 =$ _____

**THINK IT
THROUGH**

How many 25-cent stamps can
you buy with $100?

DIVIDE IN YOUR HEAD

$$1200 \div 6$$

Numbers with trailing zeros are easy to divide in your head.

$$12\,/00 \div 6$$

$$12 \div 6 = 2$$

$$2\,00$$

$$200 \times 6 = 1200$$

- CUT OFF the trailing zeros.

- DIVIDE the remaining numbers.

- TACK the trailing zeros onto your answer.

- CHECK by multiplying.

Here's how a mental-math pro thinks . . .

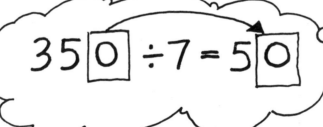

$$35\boxed{0} \div 7 = 5\boxed{0}$$

TRY THESE IN YOUR HEAD.

Watch the trailing zeros.

1. $120 \div 6$

2. $1800 \div 2$

3. $700 \div 7$

4. $9\overline{)720}$

5. $2\overline{)20{,}000}$

6. $3600 \div 36$

7. $7\overline{)770}$

8. $7\overline{)7700}$

9. $2400 \div 8$

10. $5\overline{)2500}$

POWER BUILDER A

1. 20 ÷ 2 = _____

2. 80 ÷ 4 = _____

3. 90 ÷ 3 = _____

4. 600 ÷ 3 = _____

5. 1200 ÷ 4 = _____

6. 1500 ÷ 5 = _____

7. 8)‾8000‾ = _____

8. 4000 ÷ 4 = _____

9. 3)‾6000‾ = _____

10. 6000 ÷ 2 = _____

11. 540 ÷ 6 = _____

12. 9)‾270‾ = _____

13. 180 ÷ 2 = _____

14. 250 ÷ 5 = _____

15. 7)‾630‾ = _____

16. 4900 ÷ 7 = _____

17. 12)‾1200‾ = _____

18. 4)‾20,000‾ = _____

19. 24,000 ÷ 8 = _____

20. 22,000 ÷ 2 = _____

THINK IT THROUGH

Find the largest 2-digit number that leaves a remainder of 3 when divided by 4.

POWER BUILDER B

1. 60 ÷ 3 = _____

2. 5)‾50‾ = _____

3. 80 ÷ 4 = _____

4. 1200 ÷ 2 = _____

5. 4)‾800‾ = _____

6. 1800 ÷ 3 = _____

7. 7000 ÷ 7 = _____

8. 1200 ÷ 3 = _____

9. 8000 ÷ 4 = _____

10. 3)‾9000‾ = _____

11. 540 ÷ 9 = _____

12. 360 ÷ 4 = _____

13. 3)‾180‾ = _____

14. 4)‾240‾ = _____

15. 490 ÷ 7 = _____

16. 8)‾3200‾ = _____

17. 1300 ÷ 13 = _____

18. 10,000 ÷ 5 = _____

19. 7)‾28,000‾ = _____

20. 33,000 ÷ 3 = _____

THINK IT THROUGH

Find the smallest number that does all of the following: leaves a remainder of 1 when divided by 4, leaves a remainder of 2 when divided by 5, and leaves a remainder of 3 when divided by 6.

DIVIDE IN YOUR HEAD

$$400 \div 20$$

When both numbers have trailing zeros, you can make the problem easier to do in your head.

$$40\cancel{0} \div 2\cancel{0}$$

$$40 \div 2 = 20$$

CANCEL the zeros that the numbers have in common. (In this case, we divide both numbers by 10.)

Remember, don't cancel ALL the trailing zeros. Just cancel the zeros common to both numbers.

TRY THESE IN YOUR HEAD.

Cancel the common zeros.

1. $600 \div 20$ **3.** $8000 \div 2000$ **7.** $3000 \div 200$

2. $600 \div 300$ **4.** $800 \div 20$ **8.** $5000 \div 50$

                5. $1000 \div 20$ **9.** $1200 \div 60$

                6. $9000 \div 30$ **10.** $1800 \div 200$

POWER BUILDER A

1. $80 \div 20 =$ _____
2. $60 \div 20 =$ _____
3. $90 \div 30 =$ _____
4. $120 \div 20 =$ _____
5. $150 \div 30 =$ _____
6. $270 \div 30 =$ _____
7. $360 \div 40 =$ _____
8. $480 \div 80 =$ _____
9. $500 \div 50 =$ _____
10. $800 \div 20 =$ _____

11. $900 \div 30 =$ _____
12. $1000 \div 200 =$ _____
13. $1000 \div 500 =$ _____
14. $1200 \div 200 =$ _____
15. $1800 \div 20 =$ _____
16. $6400 \div 80 =$ _____
17. $1300 \div 20 =$ _____
18. $4800 \div 30 =$ _____
19. $1360 \div 20 =$ _____
20. $1800 \div 40 =$ _____

THINK IT THROUGH

The state gets a tax of 10 cents for every dollar of gasoline sold. How much money does the state get on gasoline sales of $375,000?

POWER BUILDER B

1. $40 \div 20 =$ _____
2. $80 \div 40 =$ _____
3. $60 \div 30 =$ _____
4. $140 \div 20 =$ _____
5. $180 \div 30 =$ _____
6. $640 \div 80 =$ _____
7. $480 \div 60 =$ _____
8. $360 \div 30 =$ _____
9. $800 \div 80 =$ _____
10. $2400 \div 40 =$ _____

11. $600 \div 20 =$ _____
12. $800 \div 40 =$ _____
13. $400 \div 80 =$ _____
14. $5000 \div 500 =$ _____
15. $7000 \div 70 =$ _____
16. $4800 \div 20 =$ _____
17. $3600 \div 30 =$ _____
18. $5600 \div 400 =$ _____
19. $8400 \div 70 =$ _____
20. $7500 \div 500 =$ _____

THINK IT THROUGH

The state gets a tax of 15 cents for every dollar of gasoline sold. How much money does the state get on sales of $450,000?

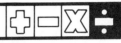

For mental division, you can simplify a problem like this one.

Here's how . . .

Break up the dividend into parts that are easily divided.

DIVIDE IN YOUR HEAD

$126 \div 3$

$12{:}6 \div 3$

$120 \div 3 = 40$
$6 \div 3 = 2$

$40 + 2 = 42$

$3 \times 42 = 126$

• BREAK UP 126 into 120 and 6.

• DIVIDE both parts by 3.

• ADD the answers.

• CHECK by multiplying.

You might see it in your mind this way . . .

START AT THE LEFT

$$\begin{array}{r} 4\;2 \\ 3\overline{)12{:}6} \end{array}$$

TRY THESE IN YOUR HEAD.

Break up the dividend.

1. $44 \div 2$ **3.** $648 \div 2$ **7.** $287 \div 7$

2. $63 \div 3$ **4.** $168 \div 8$ **8.** $248 \div 4$

                5. $324 \div 4$ **9.** $455 \div 5$

                6. $525 \div 5$ **10.** $918 \div 9$

POWER BUILDER A

1. $22 \div 2 =$ _____
2. $46 \div 2 =$ _____
3. $36 \div 3 =$ _____
4. $48 \div 4 =$ _____
5. $77 \div 7 =$ _____
6. $64 \div 2 =$ _____
7. $124 \div 2 =$ _____
8. $168 \div 8 =$ _____
9. $212 \div 2 =$ _____
10. $303 \div 3 =$ _____

11. $105 \div 5 =$ _____
12. $108 \div 2 =$ _____
13. $515 \div 5 =$ _____
14. $270 \div 3 =$ _____
15. $639 \div 3 =$ _____
16. $246 \div 2 =$ _____
17. $648 \div 6 =$ _____
18. $816 \div 8 =$ _____
19. $5005 \div 5 =$ _____
20. $2424 \div 4 =$ _____

THINK IT THROUGH

What is the remainder when you divide the sum of $90 + 91 + 92 + 93 + 94 + 95 + 96 + 97 + 98$ by 9? (Look for a shortcut!)

POWER BUILDER B

1. $28 \div 2 =$ _____
2. $68 \div 2 =$ _____
3. $77 \div 7 =$ _____
4. $86 \div 2 =$ _____
5. $39 \div 3 =$ _____
6. $146 \div 2 =$ _____
7. $147 \div 7 =$ _____
8. $155 \div 5 =$ _____
9. $333 \div 3 =$ _____
10. $124 \div 4 =$ _____

11. $126 \div 6 =$ _____
12. $714 \div 7 =$ _____
13. $404 \div 4 =$ _____
14. $640 \div 2 =$ _____
15. $848 \div 4 =$ _____
16. $749 \div 7 =$ _____
17. $918 \div 9 =$ _____
18. $248 \div 4 =$ _____
19. $8008 \div 8 =$ _____
20. $3636 \div 6 =$ _____

THINK IT THROUGH

What is the remainder when you divide the sum of $52 + 53 + 54 + 55 + 56 + 57 + 58$ by 10? (Look for a shortcut!)

106

Sometimes thinking of money can help you multiply in your head.

24×5

THINK MONEY!

24 nickels . . . It's easier to think of dimes . . .

24 nickels is $^{24}/_2$ or 12 dimes.

THE ANSWER IS 120.

24×25

THINK MONEY!

24 quarters . . . It's easier to think of dollars . . .

24 quarters is $^{24}/_4$ or 6 dollars.

THE ANSWER IS 600.

24×50

THINK MONEY!

24 half dollars . . . It's easier to think of dollars . . .

24 half dollars is $^{24}/_2$ or 12 dollars.

THE ANSWER IS 1200.

TRY THESE IN YOUR HEAD.

Think money.

1. 16×5 **3.** 12×25 **7.** 5×12

2. 5×28 **4.** 25×16 **8.** 38×5

                    5. 16×50 **9.** 50×38

                    6. 32×25 **10.** 25×12

POWER BUILDER A

1. $12 \times 5 =$ _____

2. $5 \times 18 =$ _____

3. $14 \times 50 =$ _____

4. $28 \times 25 =$ _____

5. $5 \times 88 =$ _____

6. $12 \times 50 =$ _____

7. $5 \times 48 =$ _____

8. $64 \times 50 =$ _____

9. $25 \times 32 =$ _____

10. $5 \times 36 =$ _____

11. $26 \times 50 =$ _____

12. $50 \times 36 =$ _____

13. $25 \times 64 =$ _____

14. $56 \times 5 =$ _____

15. $54 \times 50 =$ _____

16. $25 \times 240 =$ _____

17. $50 \times 220 =$ _____

18. $25 \times 44 =$ _____

19. $25 \times 180 =$ _____

20. $5 \times 222 =$ _____

THINK IT THROUGH

An ice machine makes 50 ice cubes every hour. How many cubes can it make in a day?

POWER BUILDER B

1. $14 \times 5 =$ _____

2. $5 \times 12 =$ _____

3. $18 \times 50 =$ _____

4. $48 \times 25 =$ _____

5. $5 \times 44 =$ _____

6. $28 \times 50 =$ _____

7. $5 \times 64 =$ _____

8. $48 \times 50 =$ _____

9. $36 \times 25 =$ _____

10. $5 \times 32 =$ _____

11. $22 \times 50 =$ _____

12. $50 \times 120 =$ _____

13. $25 \times 88 =$ _____

14. $54 \times 5 =$ _____

15. $56 \times 50 =$ _____

16. $25 \times 280 =$ _____

17. $50 \times 140 =$ _____

18. $25 \times 12 =$ _____

19. $25 \times 220 =$ _____

20. $5 \times 444 =$ _____

THINK IT THROUGH

An ice machine makes 25 ice cubes every hour. How many cubes can it make in a week?

MULTIPLY IN YOUR HEAD

$5 \times 7 \times 5 \times 8 \times 2 \times 2$

If you tried to do this problem one step at a time, you would bog down pretty quickly.

5 times 7 is 35, times 5 is . . . too hard!

Make your job easier!
Look for compatible pairs.

$$\begin{array}{c} \overbrace{}^{10} \\ \boxed{5} \times 7 \times \boxed{5} \times 8 \times \boxed{2} \times \boxed{2} \\ \underbrace{}_{10} \end{array}$$

Then rearrange the factors to make them easy to multiply in your head.

$$7 \times 8 \times 10 \times 10$$
$$56 \quad \times \quad 100 \ = 5600$$

TRY THESE IN YOUR HEAD.

Look for compatible pairs.

1. $2 \times 7 \times 5$

2. $2 \times 11 \times 15$

3. $4 \times 8 \times 50$

4. $4 \times 9 \times 25$

5. $6 \times 9 \times 500$

6. $400 \times 13 \times 5$

7. $25 \times 5 \times 4 \times 5$

8. $8 \times 4 \times 3 \times 250$

9. $35 \times 8 \times 2 \times 25$

10. $15 \times 3 \times 2 \times 2 \times 15$

POWER BUILDER A

1. $5 \times 3 \times 4 =$ _____

2. $2 \times 12 \times 5 =$ _____

3. $2 \times 3 \times 15 =$ _____

4. $15 \times 5 \times 4 =$ _____

5. $20 \times 7 \times 5 =$ _____

6. $2 \times 7 \times 5 \times 6 =$ _____

7. $15 \times 7 \times 2 \times 3 =$ _____

8. $6 \times 25 \times 5 \times 4 =$ _____

9. $11 \times 2 \times 4 \times 25 =$ _____

10. $25 \times 5 \times 4 \times 4 =$ _____

11. $15 \times 3 \times 3 \times 2 =$ _____

12. $4 \times 4 \times 15 \times 5 =$ _____

13. $5 \times 5 \times 9 \times 2 =$ _____

14. $5 \times 7 \times 5 \times 4 =$ _____

15. $9 \times 5 \times 3 \times 4 =$ _____

16. $13 \times 2 \times 3 \times 5 =$ _____

17. $5 \times 7 \times 7 \times 2 =$ _____

18. $5 \times 5 \times 7 \times 2 =$ _____

19. $11 \times 2 \times 3 \times 5 =$ _____

20. $9 \times 50 \times 8 \times 2 =$ _____

THINK IT THROUGH

Mentally calculate $12 \times 48 \times 0 \times 3 \times 12 \times 10$.

POWER BUILDER B

1. $4 \times 6 \times 5 =$ _____

2. $2 \times 9 \times 5 =$ _____

3. $15 \times 7 \times 2 =$ _____

4. $4 \times 9 \times 15 =$ _____

5. $5 \times 3 \times 12 =$ _____

6. $6 \times 2 \times 3 \times 5 =$ _____

7. $11 \times 2 \times 5 \times 6 =$ _____

8. $3 \times 4 \times 25 \times 9 =$ _____

9. $12 \times 25 \times 3 \times 4 =$ _____

10. $4 \times 5 \times 25 \times 4 =$ _____

11. $2 \times 3 \times 5 \times 11 =$ _____

12. $9 \times 5 \times 8 \times 2 =$ _____

13. $5 \times 3 \times 2 \times 9 =$ _____

14. $7 \times 5 \times 3 \times 4 =$ _____

15. $15 \times 4 \times 5 \times 5 =$ _____

16. $11 \times 5 \times 5 \times 8 =$ _____

17. $9 \times 5 \times 20 \times 4 =$ _____

18. $25 \times 9 \times 5 \times 4 =$ _____

19. $50 \times 9 \times 2 \times 4 =$ _____

20. $500 \times 7 \times 3 \times 2 =$ _____

THINK IT THROUGH

Mentally calculate $10 \times 36 \times 2 \times 50$.

Here's a trick that can simplify mental multiplication . . .

$$24 \times 25$$

Rearrange one or both of the numbers.

Your aim is to find compatible pairs.

$$24 \times 25$$
$$6 \times 4 \times 25$$
$$6 \times \boxed{4} \times \boxed{25} \quad \text{COMPATIBLE!}$$
$$6 \times 100 = 600$$

Can you find a different way to rearrange 24×25?

TRY THESE IN YOUR HEAD.
Rearrange to find compatible pairs.

1. 8×15 **3.** 15×16 **7.** 12×15

2. 15×24 **4.** 36×50 **8.** 18×500

5. 48×15 **9.** 12×35

6. 24×500 **10.** 15×26

POWER BUILDER A

1. $4 \times 35 =$ _____

2. $4 \times 45 =$ _____

3. $15 \times 14 =$ _____

4. $24 \times 15 =$ _____

5. $15 \times 18 =$ _____

6. $12 \times 25 =$ _____

7. $5 \times 24 =$ _____

8. $8 \times 25 =$ _____

9. $5 \times 32 =$ _____

10. $25 \times 16 =$ _____

11. $22 \times 15 =$ _____

12. $25 \times 18 =$ _____

13. $45 \times 16 =$ _____

14. $15 \times 36 =$ _____

15. $35 \times 12 =$ _____

16. $60 \times 25 =$ _____

17. $55 \times 40 =$ _____

18. $45 \times 80 =$ _____

19. $25 \times 180 =$ _____

20. $450 \times 8 =$ _____

THINK IT THROUGH

Knowing that $25 \times 25 = 625$, mentally calculate 24×25, 25×26, 25×27, and 25×23.

POWER BUILDER B

1. $6 \times 25 =$ _____

2. $35 \times 6 =$ _____

3. $55 \times 4 =$ _____

4. $6 \times 45 =$ _____

5. $45 \times 8 =$ _____

6. $6 \times 55 =$ _____

7. $45 \times 8 =$ _____

8. $8 \times 25 =$ _____

9. $15 \times 22 =$ _____

10. $25 \times 14 =$ _____

11. $25 \times 18 =$ _____

12. $25 \times 28 =$ _____

13. $45 \times 12 =$ _____

14. $15 \times 26 =$ _____

15. $35 \times 14 =$ _____

16. $40 \times 35 =$ _____

17. $50 \times 24 =$ _____

18. $250 \times 16 =$ _____

19. $40 \times 450 =$ _____

20. $15 \times 180 =$ _____

THINK IT THROUGH

Knowing that $50 \times 50 = 2500$, mentally calculate 49×50, 50×51, 48×50, and 50×52.

112

Mental Math Techniques
• **HALVE ONE, DOUBLE THE OTHER.** $4 \times 215 = ?$ $18 \times 25 = ?$
• **TACK ON TRAILING ZEROS.** $4200 \div 6 = ?$
• **CANCEL COMMON ZEROS.** $27{,}000 \div 300 = ?$
• **BREAK UP THE DIVIDEND.** $1664 \div 8 = ?$
• **THINK MONEY.** $16 \times 5 = ?$ $9 \times 25 = ?$
• **SEARCH FOR COMPATIBLES.** $50 \times 5 \times 2 \times 4 = ?$
• **MAKE YOUR OWN COMPATIBLES.** $28 \times 25 = 4 \times 7 \times 25 = ?$

Do the problems below in your head. Tell which techniques you find useful for each one.

1. 5×64
2. $1800 \div 200$
3. $6 \times 2 \times 5 \times 4$
4. 6×45
5. $515 \div 5$
6. 15×22
7. $5400/9$
8. 50×28
9. $3 \times 25 \times 2 \times 4$
10. $4000 \div 8$

Talk about each problem below. What's an easy way to do it in your head? Tell how you would think it through.

1. 56×25
2. $260 \div 13$
3. $4422 \div 11$
4. 36×5
5. 8×45
6. $36{,}000 \div 600$
7. 14×15
8. $3570 \div 7$
9. 25×16
10. $150 \times 4 \times 2 \times 30$
11. $5600 \div 70$
12. 120×8

1. Double 33 = _____

2. 217 ÷ 7 = _____

3. 4 × 6 × 50 = _____

4. 60)$\overline{4200}$ = _____

5. 25 × 24 = _____

6. 8000 ÷ 20 = _____

7. 5400/6 = _____

8. 45 × 5 × 2 × 2 = _____

9. 12 × 15 = _____

10. 240 ÷ 8 = _____

11. 8 × 24 = _____

12. 8000 ÷ 4 = _____

13. 500 × 26 = _____

14. 621/3 = _____

15. 18 × 8 = _____

16. Double 54 = _____

17. 12 × 25 = _____

18. 600 ÷ 30 = _____

19. 40)$\overline{1200}$ = _____

20. 35 × 12 = _____

21. 6300 ÷ 9 = _____

22. 50 × 42 = _____

23. Double 95 = _____

24. 50 × 46 = _____

25. 6000 ÷ 20 = _____

26. 44 × 25 = _____

27. 35)$\overline{3500}$ = _____

28. 45 × 6 = _____

29. 4 × 25 × 36 = _____

30. 369 ÷ 9 = _____

31. 8 × 35 = _____

32. 200/5 = _____

33. 40 × 5 × 0 × 6 = _____

34. 444 ÷ 4 = _____

35. Double 29 = _____

36. 11 × 5 × 2 × 9 = _____

37. Double 535 = _____

38. 5 × 48 = _____

39. 1800 ÷ 20 = _____

40. 16 × 15 = _____

1. 43 + 35 = _____

2. 68 + 32 = _____

3. 859 − 159 = _____

4. 28 + 75 = _____

5. 328 ÷ 4 = _____

6. 40 × 6 × 5 = _____

7. 3800 ÷ 10 = _____

8. 5 × 125 = _____

9. 6 × 55 = _____

10. 265 − 98 = _____

11. 80 − 24 = _____

12. 25 × 14 × 4 = _____

13. 357 + 299 = _____

14. 2000 ÷ 50 = _____

15. Double 84 = _____

16. 8 × $1.99 = _____

17. 7 × 16 = _____

18. 300 × 40 = _____

19. 5)515 = _____

20. 47 + 29 = _____

21. 5 × 54 = _____

22. 80 − 50 + 30 − 20 = _____

23. 50 × 22 = _____

24. 470 − 300 = _____

25. 2800/70 = _____

26. 55 + 29 = _____

27. 25 × 28 = _____

28. 325 + 25 + 75 = _____

29. 460 + 70 = _____

30. 8 × 99 = _____

31. 48 − 23 = _____

32. 24 × 15 = _____

33. 2600 ÷ 26 = _____

34. 165 + 19 = _____

35. 4000 × 100 = _____

36. 2 × 27 × 5 = _____

37. Double 741 = _____

38. 7000 − 4000 − 300 = _____

39. 4 × 821 = _____

40. 6140 + 500 + 2000 = _____

41. 50 × 38 = _____

42. 200)1800 = _____

43. 8 × 600 = _____

44. $20.00 − $11.98 = _____

45. 75 + 85 + 25 + 2000 = _____

46. 7 × 698 = _____

47. 3 × 74 = _____

48. 426 + 75 = _____

49. 4250 + 30 + 600 = _____

50. 8000 ÷ 2 = _____

1. 34 + 52 = _____

2. 47 + 53 = _____

3. 947 − 247 = _____

4. 28 + 175 = _____

5. 426 ÷ 6 = _____

6. 40 × 8 × 5 = _____

7. 5200 ÷ 10 = _____

8. 8 × 125 = _____

9. 6 × 65 = _____

10. 475 − 98 = _____

11. 11 × 10 = _____

12. 25 × 18 × 4 = _____

13. 463 + 299 = _____

14. 1000 ÷ 50 = _____

15. Double 74 = _____

16. 6 × $4.99 = _____

17. 9 × 16 = _____

18. 500 × 70 = _____

19. 5)525‾ = _____

20. 1000 × 5000 = _____

21. 5 × 48 = _____

22. 90 − 40 + 30 − 20 = _____

23. 50 × 14 = _____

24. 390 − 200 = _____

25. 2700/30 = _____

26. 45 + 37 = _____

27. 25 × 36 = _____

28. 125 + 25 + 75 = _____

29. 590 + 80 = _____

30. 7 × 99 = _____

31. 58 − 24 = _____

32. 24 × 15 = _____

33. 4700 ÷ 47 = _____

34. 155 + 19 = _____

35. 3000 × 100 = _____

36. 2 × 26 × 5 = _____

37. Double 253 = _____

38. 8000 − 6000 − 300 = _____

39. 3 × 623 = _____

40. 3230 + 400 + 5000 = _____

41. 50 × 28 = _____

42. 200)16,000‾ = _____

43. 9 × 700 = _____

44. $20.00 − $13.98 = _____

45. 25 + 95 + 75 + 10 = _____

46. 8 × 798 = _____

47. 5 × 26 = _____

48. 326 + 75 = _____

49. 5420 + 50 + 300 = _____

50. 6000 ÷ 2 = _____

Answer Key for Power Builders

LESSON 1

Power Builder A   **1.** 500   **2.** 900   **3.** 1100   **4.** 1500
5. 1000   **6.** 700   **7.** 1200   **8.** 1200   **9.** 8000   **10.** 12,000
11. 650   **12.** 1020   **13.** 870   **14.** 750   **15.** 730   **16.** 7400
17. 7500   **18.** 5300   **19.** 3750   **20.** 6090
Think It Through: Two possible solutions: 3 quarters and
1 nickel or 1 half dollar and 3 dimes

Power Builder B   **1.** 850   **2.** 1190   **3.** 1230   **4.** 1250
5. 890   **6.** 1440   **7.** 1420   **8.** 870   **9.** 1390   **10.** 1550
11. 7350   **12.** 1590   **13.** 5870   **14.** 10,600   **15.** 2980
16. 7750   **17.** 8280   **18.** 6150   **19.** 8700   **20.** 7120
Think It Through: 1 quarter, 2 dimes, and 2 nickels

LESSON 2

Power Builder A   **1.** 740   **2.** 570   **3.** 720   **4.** 930
5. 850   **6.** 920   **7.** 1250   **8.** 1340   **9.** 1430   **10.** 1170
11. 1670   **12.** 1590   **13.** 1030   **14.** 1290   **15.** 1260
16. 1050   **17.** 2900   **18.** 8600   **19.** 3900   **20.** 4700
Think It Through: 1009

Power Builder B   **1.** 550   **2.** 690   **3.** 820   **4.** 860
5. 980   **6.** 650   **7.** 1220   **8.** 1350   **9.** 1580   **10.** 1050
11. 1850   **12.** 1070   **13.** 1190   **14.** 1250   **15.** 1450
16. 1720   **17.** 3800   **18.** 4700   **19.** 6900   **20.** 3700
Think It Through: 1100

LESSON 3

Power Builder A   **1.** 13   **2.** 33   **3.** 343   **4.** 130   **5.** 530
6. 11   **7.** 51   **8.** 851   **9.** 15   **10.** 65   **11.** 15   **12.** 65
13. 465   **14.** 650   **15.** 350   **16.** 15   **17.** 55   **18.** 655
19. 550   **20.** 250
Think It Through: Wednesday

Power Builder B   **1.** 13   **2.** 23   **3.** 333   **4.** 130   **5.** 530
6. 13   **7.** 43   **8.** 293   **9.** 550   **10.** 250   **11.** 13   **12.** 43
13. 283   **14.** 230   **15.** 930   **16.** 11   **17.** 41   **18.** 151
19. 410   **20.** 910
Think It Through: Monday

LESSON 4

Power Builder A   **1.** 377   **2.** 778   **3.** 979   **4.** 683
5. 789   **6.** 865   **7.** 578   **8.** 795   **9.** 937   **10.** 584
11. 1036   **12.** 785   **13.** 955   **14.** 829   **15.** 574   **16.** 919
17. 878   **18.** 977   **19.** 846   **20.** 683
Think It Through: June 4

Power Builder B   **1.** 525   **2.** 766   **3.** 896   **4.** 771
5. 768   **6.** 942   **7.** 997   **8.** 847   **9.** 828   **10.** 718
11. 729   **12.** 675   **13.** 958   **14.** 699   **15.** 888   **16.** 818
17. 476   **18.** 927   **19.** 883   **20.** 699
Think It Through: Tuesday

LESSON 5

Power Builder A   **1.** 54   **2.** 73   **3.** 173   **4.** 242   **5.** 271
6. 73   **7.** 73   **8.** 91   **9.** 65   **10.** 72   **11.** 55   **12.** 42
13. 73   **14.** 75   **15.** 63   **16.** 82   **17.** 35   **18.** 93   **19.** 84
20. 46
Think It Through: 10 years old

Power Builder B   **1.** 45   **2.** 312   **3.** 52   **4.** 82   **5.** 253
6. 82   **7.** 332   **8.** 91   **9.** 92   **10.** 65   **11.** 82   **12.** 51
13. 82   **14.** 82   **15.** 51   **16.** 91   **17.** 82   **18.** 83   **19.** 77
20. 83
Think It Through: The woman is 45 and the man is 54.

LESSON 6

Power Builder A   **1.** 300   **2.** 700   **3.** 500   **4.** 600
5. 3000   **6.** 2000   **7.** 5000   **8.** 8000   **9.** 4900   **10.** 7500
11. 6300   **12.** 0   **13.** 5200   **14.** 1200   **15.** 100
16. 1000   **17.** 400   **18.** 1200   **19.** 6900   **20.** 2800
Think It Through: 90

Power Builder B   **1.** 400   **2.** 200   **3.** 600   **4.** 800
5. 3000   **6.** 3000   **7.** 6000   **8.** 6000   **9.** 2900
10. 4500   **11.** 5400   **12.** 0   **13.** 6100   **14.** 1100   **15.** 200
16. 2000   **17.** 500   **18.** 4200   **19.** 3500   **20.** 700
Think It Through: 140

LESSON 7

Power Builder A   **1.** 40   **2.** 400   **3.** 600   **4.** 630   **5.** 90
6. 60   **7.** 150   **8.** 140   **9.** 1820   **10.** 2600   **11.** 50
12. 60   **13.** 380   **14.** 900   **15.** 90   **16.** 60   **17.** 250
18. 330   **19.** 1410   **20.** 3000
Think It Through: 154

Power Builder B   **1.** 60   **2.** 70   **3.** 300   **4.** 800   **5.** 60
6. 340   **7.** 380   **8.** 20   **9.** 210   **10.** 1400   **11.** 270
12. 50   **13.** 400   **14.** 150   **15.** 210   **16.** 1020   **17.** 1700
18. 1610   **19.** 3220   **20.** 50
Think It Through: 826

LESSON 8

Power Builder A   **1.** 30   **2.** 40   **3.** 50   **4.** 40   **5.** 80
6. 10   **7.** 50   **8.** 0   **9.** 20   **10.** 60   **11.** 150   **12.** 300
13. 200   **14.** 100   **15.** 400   **16.** 330   **17.** 220   **18.** 220
19. 400   **20.** 200
Think It Through: 10

Power Builder B   **1.** 20   **2.** 50   **3.** 70   **4.** 30   **5.** 90
6. 10   **7.** 0   **8.** 50   **9.** 40   **10.** 60   **11.** 220   **12.** 100
13. 300   **14.** 800   **15.** 600   **16.** 250   **17.** 530   **18.** 440
19. 100   **20.** 500
Think It Through: 438

LESSON 9

Power Builder A **1.** 30 **2.** 50 **3.** 50 **4.** 20 **5.** 50 **6.** 10 **7.** 30 **8.** 100 **9.** 20 **10.** 90 **11.** 60 **12.** 30 **13.** 50 **14.** 20 **15.** 10 **16.** 40 **17.** 0 **18.** 30 **19.** 10 **20.** 90
Think It Through: 450

Power Builder B **1.** 90 **2.** 60 **3.** 10 **4.** 50 **5.** 30 **6.** 30 **7.** 70 **8.** 70 **9.** 80 **10.** 40 **11.** 40 **12.** 10 **13.** 40 **14.** 80 **15.** 70 **16.** 30 **17.** 70 **18.** 20 **19.** 20 **20.** 0
Think It Through: 4500

LESSON 10

Power Builder A **1.** 43 **2.** 72 **3.** 42 **4.** 90 **5.** 72 **6.** 72 **7.** 62 **8.** 81 **9.** 80 **10.** 74 **11.** 82 **12.** 43 **13.** 81 **14.** 84 **15.** 83 **16.** 52 **17.** 97 **18.** 83 **19.** 81 **20.** 55
Think It Through: April 10

Power Builder B **1.** 43 **2.** 92 **3.** 37 **4.** 81 **5.** 80 **6.** 44 **7.** 42 **8.** 56 **9.** 63 **10.** 81 **11.** 53 **12.** 66 **13.** 92 **14.** 65 **15.** 51 **16.** 87 **17.** 64 **18.** 51 **19.** 82 **20.** 65
Think It Through: Day 148

LESSON 11

Power Builder A **1.** 64 **2.** 32 **3.** 34 **4.** 25 **5.** 34 **6.** 14 **7.** 106 **8.** 323 **9.** 211 **10.** 811 **11.** 325 **12.** 164 **13.** 720 **14.** 543 **15.** 391 **16.** 4017 **17.** 7531 **18.** 1009 **19.** 6561 **20.** 9336
Think It Through: 20

Power Builder B **1.** 45 **2.** 43 **3.** 14 **4.** 34 **5.** 25 **6.** 51 **7.** 145 **8.** 250 **9.** 411 **10.** 511 **11.** 240 **12.** 530 **13.** 554 **14.** 543 **15.** 182 **16.** 2227 **17.** 1845 **18.** 6232 **19.** 7606 **20.** 9555
Think It Through: 50

LESSON 12

Power Builder A **1.** 41 **2.** 74 **3.** 83 **4.** 91 **5.** 82 **6.** 92 **7.** 113 **8.** 103 **9.** 111 **10.** 132 **11.** 151 **12.** 151 **13.** 184 **14.** 301 **15.** 492 **16.** 304 **17.** 252 **18.** 481 **19.** 502 **20.** 473
Think It Through: 65 cents

Power Builder B **1.** 52 **2.** 71 **3.** 92 **4.** 84 **5.** 83 **6.** 93 **7.** 111 **8.** 133 **9.** 121 **10.** 112 **11.** 153 **12.** 201 **13.** 152 **14.** 201 **15.** 292 **16.** 303 **17.** 251 **18.** 304 **19.** 602 **20.** 553
Think It Through: $1.45

LESSON 13

Power Builder A **1.** 62 **2.** 53 **3.** 84 **4.** 76 **5.** 72 **6.** 84 **7.** 62 **8.** 84 **9.** 61 **10.** 54 **11.** 97 **12.** 86 **13.** 76 **14.** 76 **15.** 77 **16.** 76 **17.** 87 **18.** 65 **19.** 97 **20.** 95
Think It Through: 90

Power Builder B **1.** 62 **2.** 64 **3.** 62 **4.** 94 **5.** 73 **6.** 94 **7.** 64 **8.** 72 **9.** 94 **10.** 62 **11.** 77 **12.** 76 **13.** 84 **14.** 83 **15.** 96 **16.** 84 **17.** 97 **18.** 97 **19.** 86 **20.** 87
Think It Through: 100

LESSON 14

Power Builder A **1.** 25 **2.** 25 **3.** 36 **4.** 56 **5.** 22 **6.** 28 **7.** 42 **8.** 19 **9.** 21 **10.** 14 **11.** 58 **12.** 17 **13.** 33 **14.** 56 **15.** 48 **16.** 51 **17.** 28 **18.** 45 **19.** 25 **20.** 17
Think It Through: 900

Power Builder B **1.** 33 **2.** 55 **3.** 18 **4.** 38 **5.** 43 **6.** 22 **7.** 24 **8.** 52 **9.** 37 **10.** 16 **11.** 78 **12.** 27 **13.** 33 **14.** 57 **15.** 29 **16.** 42 **17.** 17 **18.** 48 **19.** 35 **20.** 34
Think It Through: 900

LESSON 15

Power Builder A **1.** 65 **2.** 6 **3.** 69 **4.** 54 **5.** 75 **6.** 83 **7.** 47 **8.** 38 **9.** 5 **10.** 61 **11.** 600 **12.** 750 **13.** 50 **14.** 101 **15.** 625 **16.** 499 **17.** 305 **18.** 901 **19.** 275 **20.** 355
Think It Through: 51 pairs (counting the pair 50 and 50)

Power Builder B **1.** 50 **2.** 7 **3.** 51 **4.** 85 **5.** 67 **6.** 25 **7.** 92 **8.** 71 **9.** 20 **10.** 58 **11.** 300 **12.** 25 **13.** 501 **14.** 550 **15.** 905 **16.** 875 **17.** 99 **18.** 745 **19.** 350 **20.** 425
Think It Through: 26 pairs (counting the pair 50 and 50)

LESSON 16

Power Builder A **1.** 50 **2.** 100 **3.** 100 **4.** 50 **5.** 300 **6.** 200 **7.** 100 **8.** 200 **9.** 500 **10.** 200 **11.** 29 **12.** 18 **13.** 63 **14.** 52 **15.** 39 **16.** 155 **17.** 66 **18.** 35 **19.** 138 **20.** 302
Think It Through: 220

Power Builder B **1.** 100 **2.** 50 **3.** 100 **4.** 50 **5.** 100 **6.** 200 **7.** 300 **8.** 500 **9.** 200 **10.** 300 **11.** 3 **12.** 12 **13.** 55 **14.** 61 **15.** 27 **16.** 82 **17.** 56 **18.** 61 **19.** 175 **20.** 254
Think It Through: 78

LESSON 17

Power Builder A **1.** 75 **2.** 180 **3.** 135 **4.** 145 **5.** 150 **6.** 200 **7.** 175 **8.** 180 **9.** 200 **10.** 195 **11.** 75 **12.** 165 **13.** 135 **14.** 165 **15.** 175 **16.** 170 **17.** 205 **18.** 250 **19.** 175 **20.** 190
Think It Through: 900

Power Builder B **1.** 70 **2.** 145 **3.** 165 **4.** 155 **5.** 175 **6.** 185 **7.** 200 **8.** 205 **9.** 180 **10.** 190 **11.** 125 **12.** 115 **13.** 175 **14.** 125 **15.** 195 **16.** 175 **17.** 125 **18.** 155 **19.** 160 **20.** 160
Think It Through: 550

LESSON 18

Power Builder A **1.** 53 **2.** 102 **3.** 101 **4.** 153 **5.** 52 **6.** 102 **7.** 204 **8.** 303 **9.** 233 **10.** 132 **11.** 74 **12.** 133 **13.** 199 **14.** 303 **15.** 154 **16.** 283 **17.** 123 **18.** 272 **19.** 94 **20.** 274
Think It Through: 25

Power Builder B **1.** 103 **2.** 51 **3.** 152 **4.** 54 **5.** 53 **6.** 101 **7.** 103 **8.** 232 **9.** 234 **10.** 232 **11.** 73 **12.** 131 **13.** 403 **14.** 222 **15.** 153 **16.** 173 **17.** 274 **18.** 198 **19.** 374 **20.** 253
Think It Through: 0

LESSON 19

Power Builder A **1.** 100 **2.** 75 **3.** 250 **4.** 150 **5.** 350 **6.** 225 **7.** 125 **8.** 150 **9.** 375 **10.** 300 **11.** 225 **12.** 725 **13.** 525 **14.** 150 **15.** 375 **16.** 475 **17.** 550 **18.** 325 **19.** 450 **20.** 400
Think It Through: $3.75

Power Builder B **1.** 175 **2.** 100 **3.** 350 **4.** 275 **5.** 450 **6.** 325 **7.** 225 **8.** 150 **9.** 475 **10.** 400 **11.** 325 **12.** 625 **13.** 325 **14.** 250 **15.** 375 **16.** 675 **17.** 950 **18.** 425 **19.** 750 **20.** 500
Think It Through: $3.50

LESSON 20

Power Builder A **1.** 64 **2.** 103 **3.** 124 **4.** 84 **5.** 85 **6.** 224 **7.** 921 **8.** 906 **9.** 943 **10.** 1823 **11.** $5.21 **12.** $1.73 **13.** $4.83 **14.** $16.33 **15.** $17.43 **16.** $6.24 **17.** $1.63 **18.** $4.34 **19.** $24.43 **20.** $15.97
Think It Through: 77 cents

Power Builder B **1.** 74 **2.** 91 **3.** 143 **4.** 253 **5.** 466 **6.** 855 **7.** 2844 **8.** 597 **9.** 4754 **10.** 573 **11.** $1.25 **12.** $4.44 **13.** $1.85 **14.** $2.43 **15.** $9.51 **16.** $18.64 **17.** $17.73 **18.** $25.34 **19.** $75.85 **20.** $26.73
Think It Through: $9.00

LESSON 21

Power Builder A **1.** 53 **2.** 26 **3.** 167 **4.** 25 **5.** 53 **6.** 247 **7.** 525 **8.** 517 **9.** 48 **10.** 755 **11.** $3.01 **12.** $4.02 **13.** $1.01 **14.** $6.02 **15.** $10.02 **16.** $5.01 **17.** $2.02 **18.** $5.01 **19.** $20.01 **20.** $15.02
Think It Through: $2.02

Power Builder B **1.** 35 **2.** 34 **3.** 27 **4.** 47 **5.** 136 **6.** 528 **7.** 554 **8.** 3528 **9.** 1301 **10.** 1552 **11.** $0.16 **12.** $0.22 **13.** $1.02 **14.** $5.02 **15.** $4.01 **16.** $50.01 **17.** $30.02 **18.** $7.02 **19.** $11.01 **20.** $31.01
Think It Through: $1.04

LESSON 22

Power Builder A **1.** 20 **2.** 50 **3.** 70 **4.** 400 **5.** 300 **6.** 5000 **7.** 7000 **8.** 2000 **9.** 800 **10.** 90 **11.** 110 **12.** 270 **13.** 1250 **14.** 2300 **15.** 6900 **16.** 12,500 **17.** 13,000 **18.** 18,000 **19.** 275,000 **20.** 51,000
Think It Through: $9.00

Power Builder B **1.** 40 **2.** 60 **3.** 30 **4.** 200 **5.** 600 **6.** 3000 **7.** 6000 **8.** 4000 **9.** 700 **10.** 1500 **11.** 130 **12.** 190 **13.** 250 **14.** 2700 **15.** 7300 **16.** 37,500 **17.** 19,000 **18.** 375,000 **19.** 12,000 **20.** 68,000
Think It Through: 25¢

LESSON 23

Power Builder A **1.** 320 **2.** 490 **3.** 810 **4.** 240 **5.** 360 **6.** 2000 **7.** 4500 **8.** 4800 **9.** 2400 **10.** 2400 **11.** 27,000 **12.** 8000 **13.** 24,000 **14.** 49,000 **15.** 48,000 **16.** 42,000 **17.** 720 **18.** 2500 **19.** 56,000 **20.** 1600
Think It Through: 25 dimes

Power Builder B **1.** 640 **2.** 70 **3.** 270 **4.** 320 **5.** 240 **6.** 2500 **7.** 1800 **8.** 1600 **9.** 900 **10.** 7700 **11.** 28,000 **12.** 40,000 **13.** 16,000 **14.** 21,000 **15.** 44,000 **16.** 3600 **17.** 540 **18.** 20,000 **19.** 5600 **20.** 32,000
Think It Through: 20 dimes

LESSON 24

Power Builder A **1.** 100 **2.** 400 **3.** 2000 **4.** 8100 **5.** 4200 **6.** 10,000 **7.** 12,000 **8.** 9000 **9.** 25,000 **10.** 56,000 **11.** 250,000 **12.** 210,000 **13.** 80,000 **14.** 10,000 **15.** 810,000 **16.** 20,000 **17.** 160,000 **18.** 300,000 **19.** 320,000 **20.** 800,000
Think It Through: 1800 times

Power Builder B **1.** 1600 **2.** 600 **3.** 2800 **4.** 6400 **5.** 6300 **6.** 10,000 **7.** 12,000 **8.** 8000 **9.** 9000 **10.** 56,000 **11.** 360,000 **12.** 210,000 **13.** 50,000 **14.** 20,000 **15.** 640,000 **16.** 40,000 **17.** 160,000 **18.** 300,000 **19.** 320,000 **20.** 700,000
Think It Through: 4800 times

LESSON 25

Power Builder A **1.** 217 **2.** 123 **3.** 88 **4.** 249 **5.** 255 **6.** 498 **7.** 752 **8.** 290 **9.** 156 **10.** 112 **11.** 464 **12.** 396 **13.** 192 **14.** 192 **15.** 539 **16.** 118 **17.** 357 **18.** 1230 **19.** 750 **20.** 2200
Think It Through: 9 and 11

Power Builder B **1.** 147 **2.** 82 **3.** 66 **4.** 168 **5.** 204 **6.** 444 **7.** 747 **8.** 325 **9.** 174 **10.** 165 **11.** 180 **12.** 275 **13.** 290 **14.** 152 **15.** 576 **16.** 96 **17.** 342 **18.** 1560 **19.** 500 **20.** 2250
Think It Through: 1 and 19

LESSON 26

Power Builder A **1.** 868 **2.** 605 **3.** 496 **4.** 270 **5.** 975 **6.** 2121 **7.** 1881 **8.** 4806 **9.** 2525 **10.** 999 **11.** 870 **12.** 825 **13.** 940 **14.** 4200 **15.** 1024 **16.** 369 **17.** 2100 **18.** 2500 **19.** 4040 **20.** 3030
Think It Through: The answer always has four digits, the first two digits being the same as the last two digits.

Power Builder B   **1.** 688   **2.** 610   **3.** 492   **4.** 296
5. 1275   **6.** 2828   **7.** 1236   **8.** 4806   **9.** 3525   **10.** 1038
11. 690   **12.** 725   **13.** 830   **14.** 3400   **15.** 1020   **16.** 639
17. 2020   **18.** 1269   **19.** 470   **20.** 2799
Think It Through: 472,472; 203,203; 47,047

LESSON 27

Power Builder A   **1.** 316   **2.** 632   **3.** 237   **4.** 474
5. 158   **6.** 1592   **7.** 2394   **8.** 2995   **9.** 2397   **10.** 3998
11. $39.95   **12.** $79.98   **13.** $47.96   **14.** $59.97
15. $55.93   **16.** $8.97   **17.** $99.95   **18.** $7.96
19. $59.85   **20.** $249.95
Think It Through: 403

Power Builder B   **1.** 312   **2.** 354   **3.** 356   **4.** 395
5. 203   **6.** 232   **7.** 2994   **8.** 3495   **9.** 2697   **10.** 8997
11. $23.94   **12.** $59.97   **13.** $119.98   **14.** $13.93
15. $27.96   **16.** $11.94   **17.** $29.97   **18.** $149.95
19. $35.98   **20.** $49.75
Think It Through: 196

LESSON 28

Power Builder A   **1.** 46   **2.** 124   **3.** 420   **4.** 414   **5.** 90
6. 1016   **7.** 114   **8.** 196   **9.** 500   **10.** 1800   **11.** 84
12. 182   **13.** 650   **14.** 72   **15.** 110   **16.** 172   **17.** 128
18. 256   **19.** 512   **20.** 1024
Think It Through: Let x = any number. Then
$\frac{2x + 6}{2} - x = 3$.

Power Builder B   **1.** 86   **2.** 148   **3.** 226   **4.** 32   **5.** 170
6. 1400   **7.** 174   **8.** 194   **9.** 130   **10.** 1680   **11.** 68
12. 166   **13.** 848   **14.** 818   **15.** 150   **16.** 54   **17.** 108
18. 216   **19.** 432   **20.** 864
Think It Through: Answer is always the starting number.
Let x = any number. Then $\frac{4x - 8}{4} + 2 = x$.

LESSON 29

Power Builder A   **1.** 52   **2.** 90   **3.** 280   **4.** 92   **5.** 210
6. 220   **7.** 390   **8.** 120   **9.** 148   **10.** 150   **11.** 210
12. 480   **13.** 350   **14.** 450   **15.** 4000   **16.** 900   **17.** 2100
18. 1000   **19.** 490   **20.** 1800
Think It Through: 128 × 16

Power Builder B   **1.** 56   **2.** 150   **3.** 360   **4.** 96   **5.** 270
6. 260   **7.** 330   **8.** 440   **9.** 188   **10.** 450   **11.** 270
12. 400   **13.** 960   **14.** 360   **15.** 1800   **16.** 1200
17. 192   **18.** 750   **19.** 630   **20.** 1800
Think It Through: 96 × 72

LESSON 30

Power Builder A   **1.** 10   **2.** 10   **3.** 8   **4.** 3   **5.** 7   **6.** 20
7. 2   **8.** 10   **9.** 3   **10.** 40   **11.** 50   **12.** 8   **13.** 70
14. 100   **15.** 9   **16.** 90   **17.** 60   **18.** 900   **19.** 700
20. 80
Think It Through: 40 stamps

Power Builder B   **1.** 5   **2.** 10   **3.** 9   **4.** 5   **5.** 60   **6.** 20
7. 2   **8.** 6   **9.** 3   **10.** 40   **11.** 60   **12.** 6   **13.** 60   **14.** 100
15. 60   **16.** 70   **17.** 50   **18.** 900   **19.** 900   **20.** 900
Think It Through: 400 stamps

LESSON 31

Power Builder A   **1.** 10   **2.** 20   **3.** 30   **4.** 200   **5.** 300
6. 300   **7.** 1000   **8.** 1000   **9.** 2000   **10.** 3000   **11.** 90
12. 30   **13.** 90   **14.** 50   **15.** 90   **16.** 700   **17.** 100
18. 5000   **19.** 3000   **20.** 11,000
Think It Through: 99

Power Builder B   **1.** 20   **2.** 10   **3.** 20   **4.** 600   **5.** 200
6. 600   **7.** 1000   **8.** 400   **9.** 2000   **10.** 3000   **11.** 60
12. 90   **13.** 60   **14.** 60   **15.** 70   **16.** 400   **17.** 100
18. 2000   **19.** 4000   **20.** 11,000
Think It Through: 57

LESSON 32

Power Builder A   **1.** 4   **2.** 3   **3.** 3   **4.** 6   **5.** 5   **6.** 9
7. 9   **8.** 6   **9.** 10   **10.** 40   **11.** 30   **12.** 5   **13.** 2   **14.** 6
15. 90   **16.** 80   **17.** 65   **18.** 160   **19.** 68   **20.** 45
Think It Through: $37,500

Power Builder B   **1.** 2   **2.** 2   **3.** 2   **4.** 7   **5.** 6   **6.** 8
7. 8   **8.** 12   **9.** 10   **10.** 60   **11.** 30   **12.** 20   **13.** 5
14. 10   **15.** 100   **16.** 240   **17.** 120   **18.** 14   **19.** 120
20. 15
Think It Through: $67,500

LESSON 33

Power Builder A   **1.** 11   **2.** 23   **3.** 12   **4.** 12   **5.** 11
6. 32   **7.** 62   **8.** 21   **9.** 106   **10.** 101   **11.** 21   **12.** 54
13. 103   **14.** 90   **15.** 213   **16.** 123   **17.** 108   **18.** 102
19. 1001   **20.** 606
Think It Through: 0

Power Builder B   **1.** 14   **2.** 34   **3.** 11   **4.** 43   **5.** 13
6. 73   **7.** 21   **8.** 31   **9.** 111   **10.** 31   **11.** 21   **12.** 102
13. 101   **14.** 320   **15.** 212   **16.** 107   **17.** 102   **18.** 62
19. 1001   **20.** 606
Think It Through: 5

LESSON 34

Power Builder A   **1.** 60   **2.** 90   **3.** 700   **4.** 700   **5.** 440
6. 600   **7.** 240   **8.** 3200   **9.** 800   **10.** 180   **11.** 1300
12. 1800   **13.** 1600   **14.** 280   **15.** 2700   **16.** 6000
17. 11,000   **18.** 1100   **19.** 4500   **20.** 1110
Think It Through: 1200 cubes

Power Builder B   **1.** 70   **2.** 60   **3.** 900   **4.** 1200   **5.** 220
6. 1400   **7.** 320   **8.** 2400   **9.** 900   **10.** 160   **11.** 1100
12. 6000   **13.** 2200   **14.** 270   **15.** 2800   **16.** 7000
17. 7000   **18.** 300   **19.** 5500   **20.** 2220
Think It Through: 4200 cubes

LESSON 35

Power Builder A **1.** 60 **2.** 120 **3.** 90 **4.** 300 **5.** 700 **6.** 420 **7.** 630 **8.** 3000 **9.** 2200 **10.** 2000 **11.** 270 **12.** 1200 **13.** 450 **14.** 700 **15.** 540 **16.** 390 **17.** 490 **18.** 350 **19.** 330 **20.** 7200

Think It Through: 0

Power Builder B **1.** 120 **2.** 90 **3.** 210 **4.** 540 **5.** 180 **6.** 180 **7.** 660 **8.** 2700 **9.** 3600 **10.** 2000 **11.** 330 **12.** 720 **13.** 270 **14.** 420 **15.** 1500 **16.** 2200 **17.** 3600 **18.** 4500 **19.** 3600 **20.** 21,000

Think It Through: 36,000

LESSON 36

Power Builder A **1.** 140 **2.** 180 **3.** 210 **4.** 360 **5.** 270 **6.** 300 **7.** 120 **8.** 200 **9.** 160 **10.** 400 **11.** 330 **12.** 450 **13.** 720 **14.** 540 **15.** 420 **16.** 1500 **17.** 2200 **18.** 3600 **19.** 4500 **20.** 3600

Think It Through: 600; 650; 675; 575

Power Builder B **1.** 150 **2.** 210 **3.** 220 **4.** 270 **5.** 360 **6.** 330 **7.** 360 **8.** 200 **9.** 330 **10.** 350 **11.** 450 **12.** 700 **13.** 540 **14.** 390 **15.** 490 **16.** 1400 **17.** 1200 **18.** 4000 **19.** 18,000 **20.** 2700

Think It Through: 2450; 2550; 2400; 2600

Answer Key for Tests

UNIT ONE PROGRESS TEST

1. 730 **2.** 1040 **3.** 65 **4.** 3600 **5.** 88 **6.** 500 **7.** 60 **8.** 530 **9.** 93 **10.** 640 **11.** 88 **12.** 320 **13.** 930 **14.** 2300 **15.** 43 **16.** 5480 **17.** 320 **18.** 3800 **19.** 60 **20.** 488 **21.** 1720 **22.** 60 **23.** 6500 **24.** 668 **25.** 2400 **26.** 610 **27.** 84 **28.** 3300 **29.** 320 **30.** 4370 **31.** 70 **32.** 1750 **33.** 85 **34.** 67 **35.** 84 **36.** 2150 **37.** 1700 **38.** 587 **39.** 700 **40.** 82

UNIT TWO PROGRESS TEST

1. 145 **2.** 94 **3.** 9 **4.** 64 **5.** 975 **6.** 23 **7.** 36 **8.** 154 **9.** 81 **10.** 77 **11.** 95 **12.** 623 **13.** 92 **14.** 57 **15.** 55 **16.** 200 **17.** 241 **18.** 63 **19.** 28 **20.** 74 **21.** 56 **22.** 138 **23.** 56 **24.** 62 **25.** 270 **26.** 174 **27.** 24 **28.** 16 **29.** 250 **30.** 261 **31.** 154 **32.** 75 **33.** 302 **34.** 175 **35.** 2802 **36.** 59 **37.** 218 **38.** 64 **39.** 85 **40.** 100

UNIT THREE PROGRESS TEST

1. 2500 **2.** 1272 **3.** 244 **4.** 104 **5.** 36 **6.** 175 **7.** 240 **8.** $58.24 **9.** 15,000 **10.** 2800 **11.** 104 **12.** 4800 **13.** 150 **14.** 365 **15.** 165 **16.** 4836 **17.** 66 **18.** 313 **19.** 5000 **20.** 3276 **21.** 325 **22.** 2200 **23.** $14.95 **24.** $4.02 **25.** 510 **26.** 400 **27.** 5400 **28.** $13.97 **29.** 600 **30.** 350 **31.** 3600 **32.** 380 **33.** $7.47 **34.** $55.98 **35.** 194 **36.** 9000 **37.** 800 **38.** $6.02 **39.** 4317 **40.** 4792

UNIT FOUR PROGRESS TEST

1. 66 **2.** 31 **3.** 1200 **4.** 70 **5.** 600 **6.** 400 **7.** 900 **8.** 900 **9.** 180 **10.** 30 **11.** 192 **12.** 2000 **13.** 13,000 **14.** 207 **15.** 144 **16.** 108 **17.** 300 **18.** 20 **19.** 30 **20.** 420 **21.** 700 **22.** 2100 **23.** 190 **24.** 2300 **25.** 300 **26.** 1100 **27.** 100 **28.** 270 **29.** 3600 **30.** 41 **31.** 280 **32.** 40 **33.** 0 **34.** 111 **35.** 58 **36.** 990 **37.** 1070 **38.** 240 **39.** 90 **40.** 240

CUMULATIVE TEST, FORM A

1. 78 **2.** 100 **3.** 700 **4.** 103 **5.** 82 **6.** 1200 **7.** 380 **8.** 625 **9.** 330 **10.** 167 **11.** 56 **12.** 1400 **13.** 656 **14.** 40 **15.** 168 **16.** $15.92 **17.** 112 **18.** 12,000 **19.** 103 **20.** 76 **21.** 270 **22.** 40 **23.** 1100 **24.** 170 **25.** 40 **26.** 84 **27.** 700 **28.** 425 **29.** 530 **30.** 792 **31.** 25 **32.** 360 **33.** 100 **34.** 184 **35.** 400,000 **36.** 270 **37.** 1482 **38.** 2700 **39.** 3284 **40.** 8640 **41.** 1900 **42.** 9 **43.** 4800 **44.** $8.02 **45.** 2185 **46.** 4886 **47.** 222 **48.** 501 **49.** 4880 **50.** 4000

CUMULATIVE TEST, FORM B

1. 86 **2.** 100 **3.** 700 **4.** 203 **5.** 71 **6.** 1600 **7.** 520 **8.** 1000 **9.** 390 **10.** 377 **11.** 110 **12.** 1800 **13.** 762 **14.** 20 **15.** 148 **16.** $29.94 **17.** 144 **18.** 35,000 **19.** 105 **20.** 5,000,000 **21.** 240 **22.** 60 **23.** 700 **24.** 190 **25.** 90 **26.** 82 **27.** 900 **28.** 225 **29.** 670 **30.** 693 **31.** 34 **32.** 360 **33.** 100 **34.** 174 **35.** 300,000 **36.** 260 **37.** 506 **38.** 1700 **39.** 1869 **40.** 8630 **41.** 1400 **42.** 80 **43.** 6300 **44.** $6.02 **45.** 205 **46.** 6384 **47.** 130 **48.** 401 **49.** 5770 **50.** 3000